I Will Need To Break Your Other Leg

This book is dedicated to Lily

I Will Need To Break Your Other Leg

tales of medical adventure and misadventure

Prasanna Gautam

Hammersmith Press
London

First published in 2008 by Hammersmith Press Limited,
496 Fulham Palace Road, London SW6 6JD, UK
ww.hammersmithpress.co.uk

Author's note: Where I have included case histories, descriptions of patients, or dialogue, usually recreated from memory after many years or even decades, I have taken considerable care in each case to protect the identity of the people involved. I have changed a variety of medical, personal, historical and other identifying details, including sometimes the time, place and circumstances of the encounter – in some cases blending similar stories together. Despite this occasional but very necessary 'fictionalisation' to protect identity, every single one of the stories is based originally on real people and on real events. I am very grateful to the people concerned, and I hope that I have described them with the respect and compassion that they deserve. I am also confident that anyone who thinks they recognise themselves in the narrative will be mistaken, for I have deliberately created characters that are in some ways archetypal.

British Library Cataloguing in Publication Data:
A CIP record of this book is available from the British Library.

ISBN 978-1-905140-21-3

Designed by Amina Dudhia
Typeset by Phoenix Photosetting
Production by Helen Whitehorn, Pathmedia
Printed and bound by TJ International Ltd, Padstow, Cornwall, UK

CONTENTS

ACKNOWLEDGEMENTS

Nandan and Meena, who always seemed fascinated by the stories in medicine, encouraged me to write an autobiography including these tales. I did not think that the story of my life would be more interesting than paying tribute to my patients in this manner. I must therefore thank both my children and my patients.

I must acknowledge with profound gratitude my mentors who made me the kind of doctor that I eventually became. There are many but I would like to say special thanks to the late John Edge, and also to Malcolm Palmer, Norman Coulshed, Alex Harley, Michael Lye and Ray Tallis. And finally, to Georgina Bentliff of Hammersmith Press who found my work sufficiently interesting to publish.

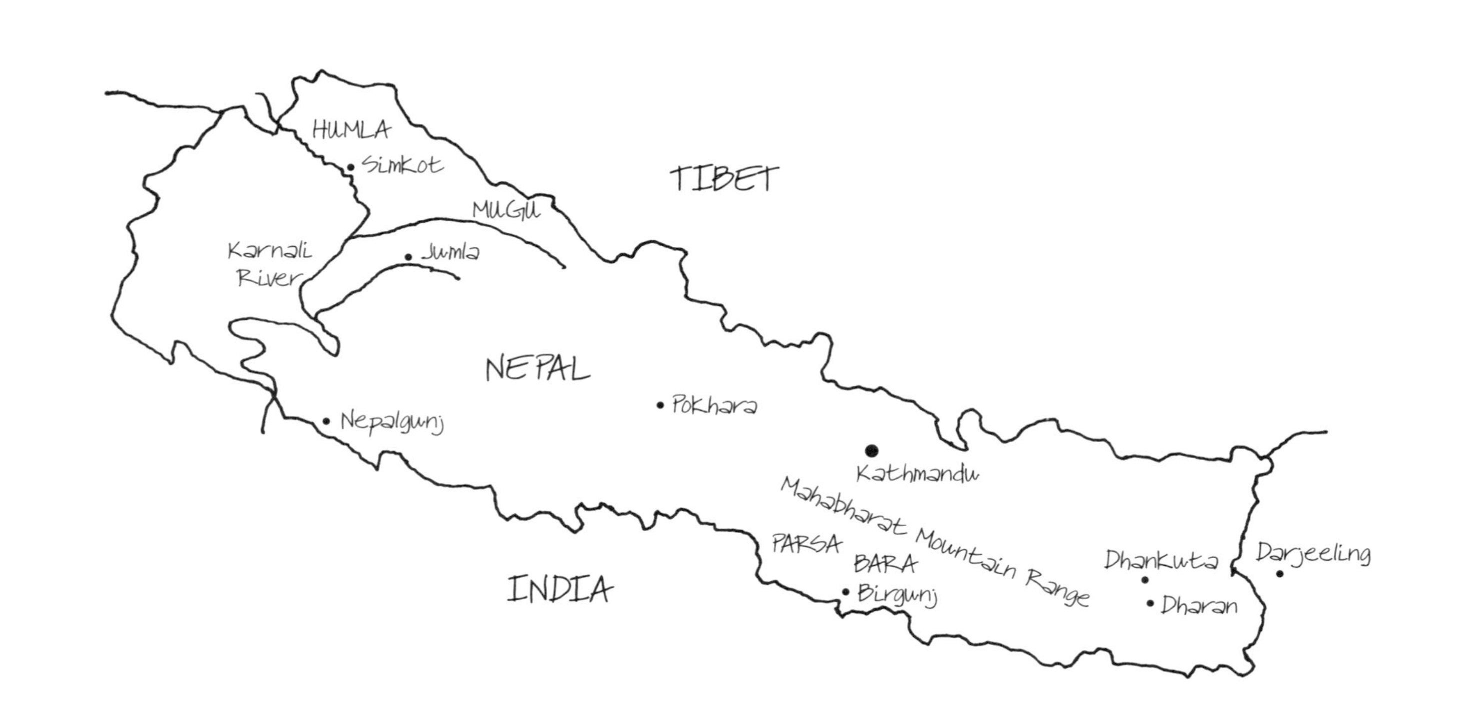
HUMLA
Simkot
TIBET
MUGU
Karnali
River
Jumla
NEPAL
Nepalgunj
Pokhara
Kathmandu
Mahabharat Mountain Range
PARSA
BARA
Birgunj
INDIA
Dhankuta
Dharan
Darjeeling

PREFACE

I have never kept a diary but have a good memory and rarely forget important information or events. When I set out to write this book, I jotted down about one hundred incidents, making a long list. This brought back many painful as well as profoundly sublime moments, including numerous memorable patients who had helped to shape my destiny. At the beginning, the working title of the book was simply 'On being a doctor'. During the course of writing it became apparent that I was talking about both my own feelings and experiences and those of my patients and about how these interacted. So the working title became 'It works both ways'. Finally, the book has resolved itself into an anthology of unique medical adventures, and misadventures; the final title is based on a chapter with more than its fair share of misadventures, as you will see. Of the original long list, I have selected only twenty-five stories that to me stand out as seminal moments in my development as a doctor and as a person.

Each story stands alone so you can start reading from any chapter, though the incidents are largely in chronological order. I have described the relevant social, political, religious and professional background to each because I have learnt that no medical problem can be properly understood or treated without reference to its wider context. Holistic medicine means considering a patient's total life circumstances as part of the problem, and the solution.

It has been essential to maintain the anonymity of my patients. Hence all personal details in the book, apart from those of my family, have been changed, as have many place names and chronological aspects. However, the central facts are true and the messages I have taken from them unequivocal. It is the nutrients in the meal and not the seasoning that impart nourishment. In these times of constant change in health care provision and medical education, my aim is, through the essence of these stories, to stimulate all those involved in patient care to think laterally and do nothing by rote but always to put the interests of the patient first. At worst, the book will be seen as an amusing collection of bizarre events. The reader will have to decide.

Two common themes run through these narratives: the need for the doctor to think for him/herself on the basis of sound knowledge and careful observation; and the importance of the doctor-patient relationship as something that involves give and take on both sides.

It is the responsibility of a doctor to do the best for a patient in spite of any adverse circumstance that may be prevailing at the time. A doctor must improvise at times, show ingenuity at all times, stand up to any adverse influences, be prepared to take risks and do whatever is possible for the benefit of the patient. He, or she, must follow these principles even in the most unlikely situations because they are fundamental to the special relationship between doctor and patient. These principles are being challenged today by the drive towards super-specialisation and 'cure' rather than healing and succour.

There is a lot more to the doctor-patient relationship than is generally acknowledged. This is a special bond, which must be kept relatively weak in the interests of objectivity. Nevertheless, it is the catalyst for creativity in medicine – for making medicine an art as well as a science. This is manifest when a doctor not only treats a specific disease but also cares for a patient as a whole human being. Little acknowledged, but experienced by all doctors, is the influence that patients have on their doctors, sometimes subtly, and sometimes overtly. I have been profoundly influenced by my patients throughout my career.

I believe that the science of medicine is the essential foundation, or broad canvas, upon which the art of medicine can be created. Each encounter with a patient then becomes a unique work, which cannot be replicated but from which much can be learned for the future. This is the beauty and the challenge of medicine.

Prasanna Gautam
Aberdeen, 2008

PART I

Starting Out

CHAPTER 1

Too Little, Too Late

'I hate New Year's Eve,' announced Dr Ahamad, a junior staff anaesthetist, from the head of the operating table.

'Booze, fornication and every known sin is committed on this day, and they call it fun. Ha! Allah protect us.' He looked at the ceiling and perhaps cursed silently. He continued his work of anaesthetising the patient. It was easy to see that he was tired, irritable and unhappy.

I wanted to ask if he was alright, simply to be polite and to make conversation, but I did not. Instead, I grunted something unintelligible. Dr Ahamad continued with his soliloquy. No doubt he was predicting hell and the wrath of Allah on all those debauchers. Somehow I could not sympathise with him although he like me had been continuously on call since Friday morning. New Year's Eve had always been my favourite event and I saw no reason to condemn it even though some clearly misused it. It was now four AM on New Year's Day, which was a Sunday. This was the last weekend of 'on call' for me as a rotating Intern in Surgery at Victoria Hospital, Bangalore.

I was waiting for Dr Ahamad to tell me that the patient was fully anaesthetised and ready for the operation.

The patient was a thirty-three year-old milkman. He had been on his nightly delivery to the many tea shops and *dhabas* (roadside eateries) which would open at about four AM for the truckers and other early birds. As was customary in those days, he was carrying two twenty-gallon drums of milk perilously attached on either side of the rear wheel of his pedal bicycle. He happened to skid over a small mound of cow dung and careered into the main carriageway. One of the trucks hit his bicycle from behind. He had fallen with his right arm stretched out on the road. Unluckily for him, the left rear wheel of the truck had rolled over his right hand.

He had been brought to the Emergency Department of Victoria Hospital by a kindly passerby in his car. The accident had occurred just outside Bangalore on Mysore Road. I had received him straight away. He was howling with pain, had lost a lot of blood and was rapidly sinking into a state of shock. The hand was badly mangled, the tendons and nerves were all exposed and hanging out amidst spurting blood, cow dung and clots. I had given him a shot of pethidine, and immediately taken him to the operating theatre. There I had set up an intravenous line and taken samples of blood for routine tests and cross-matching for possible blood transfusion. Haemaccil, a colloid infusion, was then started to maintain his circulation and blood pressure. The emergency room Sister had had the foresight to apply the cuff of a sphygmomanometer (blood pressure gauge) as a tourniquet. I had then left him in the care of the nurses, asking them to bandage his hand with ice, and gone to look for my seniors. The top priority was to save his hand from being amputated. Any delay would certainly lead to that catastrophe.

I knew that the Duty Registrar and the Senior Resident were desperately battling to save a patient with an abdominal injury and ruptured spleen in the adjoining theatre. Another surgical intern was assisting them. That meant I needed to get the Lecturer, the most senior surgeon in the department that night, who was rarely ever disturbed while on duty. It was not done to send an orderly to inform a senior colleague; one had to go in person and present the case respectfully. Only then would the learned doctor condescend to see the patient if appropriate. Only the very junior doctors like me were called by phone or through the hospital announcement system. (There were no pagers in those days.) Protocols had to be observed very strictly if one cared to get a good reference at the end of one's tenure in that surgical firm. A lecturer could make or break your career.

I was attached to the firm of Dr Malappa, a junior professor of surgery. He hardly operated in Victoria Hospital but was rumoured to be very good. He mostly taught and helped with the complicated conditions in the major operating theatre. He was reputed to have a huge private practice. His assistant, the Lecturer, managed the firm. He was supported by two middle-ranking doctors – a registrar and a third-year surgical resident trainee – who conducted most of the operations. Then there were the three of us minions (the interns) – one manned the ward, another worked in the minor operating theatre and the third assisted in the main theatre. We worked from about seven in the morning until eight in the evening when the 'doctors on call' would take over, except at 'weekends on call' when we would be working continuously. I had hated every day of the last four weeks of this surgical rotation even though I had been able to perform a lot of surgery under supervision – close an abdomen, assist in a vasectomy, do an appendicectomy, and undertake many small procedures in the minor and major operating theatres. I had not received a single word of encouragement no matter how hard I tried to do well. Two more weeks and I would move on to General Medicine. What joy!

I reached the staff room, which by then had become quiet. Festivities had ceased. Most doctors there were drowsy; it was hard to tell whether it was due to alcohol or genuine fatigue. The Lecturer in Surgery was gently snoring. I woke him up and briefly presented the case of the victim of the road traffic accident. It must have been the earlier celebrations which made him tell me to 'F*** off, go and stitch the bastard'. He glared at me, asking how many more times should he tell those 'f***ing milkmen' not to transport milk that way on their bicycles. He was sick of it, he said. He then fell asleep. I had not known that this kind of accident was common.

The hand was in a mess; it was clearly a job for a senior and experienced surgeon, not for an intern like me. Just as clearly, the Lecturer was in no fit state to perform the delicate repair work required for this patient. But there was no one else. My main concern was that unless operated on immediately the hand would have to be amputated. I retreated. Could I repair this hand? How could he have told me to do the repair myself? I could not help but remember what he had said to me a few months earlier when I was a final-year student.

He was frothing at the mouth with venom and ridiculing me in front of our group of final-year medical students. It was meant to be a symposium on brain tumours but he had decided to make it a session on head injuries instead, for which we were not prepared. I had not been able to explain fully the 'false localising sign' in head injuries. Then he had asked me a question about the course of the sixth cranial nerve which controls the side movements of the eye ball. I described its course correctly but made a small mistake on its precise relationship with the third cranial nerve at its foramina (small opening) of exit from the skull.

'Get the brain of a cadaver from Abhayia [the morgue technician in the anatomy dissecting room of the medical school], tie it on your head and run around the big courtyard four times – you might get some brains! What an idiot! *You will never make a surgeon,*' he had said. The whole class had burst into uncomfortable laughter; Dr Ramasamy, the Lecturer in Surgery, laughing the loudest of all at his own wit.

How I hated the guy.

The department of surgery had six 'firms', each led by a professor and his staff, many of whom could compete to become the angels of *Yamaraj* – the Hindu god of death. They appeared so arrogant and filled with self-importance that none of them could have inspired any student to become a surgeon. No student was spared humiliation and insult by Dr Ramasamy and his colleagues. The girl students would burst into tears in the classroom. Even Ramesh, the most dedicated student whose only reason for studying medicine was to become a cardiac surgeon, used to get doubts about his vocation. Thank god, he left for New York as soon as the results were announced and was thus spared the humiliation of working as an intern in the surgical department. He had come first in the final surgery examination followed by the slimmest of margins by myself. By right, I now had first refusal on a traineeship in surgery. No thank you. I had already decided to become a physician.

'It will be your fault if he ends up with an amputation, Ramasamy, you degenerate drunken so-and-so,' I cursed him silently. I shuddered at the vision of this milkman, minus his right hand, begging, next to a *dhaba,* his young children, naked, playing in the dirt by the kerb and his wife sweeping the footpath! It was all up to me now.

'OK now, all yours,' said Dr Ahamad, motioning to the patient lying upon the operating table. His right arm was placed over an arm rest. I was scrubbed, gowned, masked and ready. The theatre sister faced me across the table with her tray of instruments, swabs and a horde of all kinds of implements that might be necessary during the operation.

It took some considerable time for the two nurses and me to clean the injured hand with warm soapy water and saline. The closed arteries began to spurt and the veins opened up, making it messy. We increased the pressure over the tourniquet which made the veins bleed more. He could not afford to buy blood and none of his relatives who might be able to do so, or to be donors, had yet been informed of the accident. We tried to be as fast as we could but it was not easy to get rid of the grime and cow dung from the wound. I needed to change my gloves and gown in the process.

Finally, I was ready to begin. I began by examining the damage methodically. The palm had taken the full weight and movement of the wheel of the truck. Bits of skin were already dead. This would need debridement – that is, the dead skin needed to be carefully removed. The deep palmar fascia, the shiny tough covering which protects the sinews, nerves and tendons deep inside the hand, was lacerated and torn. The flexor tendons, which bend the fingers, were visible. One of these was lacerated badly and severed. A few others were shredded but not severed. The flexor hallucis tendon that bends the thumb was badly bruised. The fingers were not too bad. The nerves looked like a tangle of glistening twine and I gave up trying to trace and separate each branch. The palmar arch, the configuration of arteries that supply blood to the fingers, was lacerated and gently oozing blood, despite the tourniquet. The third and fourth metacarpals, the short narrow bones of the palm, were broken at multiple sites. My heart sank. It was very likely that this hand would need to be amputated.

I had never assisted at hand surgery, nor done any plastic surgical training, yet I had no choice but to operate and try to save this man's hand. I had no idea how I was going to do this. I silently prayed to Lord Vishnu, in the form of Lord Venkateshwara Balaji of Tirupati, who had restored my self-confidence many times during the difficult days of my studentship. I took a deep breath and stretched out my hand for the first instrument to begin the operation.

I became oblivious to the outside world. The Theatre Sister and I worked somehow in complete unison. She anticipated my every need. I was unaware of the other nurse who continuously mopped my brow. My knowledge of anatomy came back. Was I possessed? I sewed as neatly as possible all that needed sewing. I darned as delicately as I dared. I realigned the broken bones and secured them with thick silk loops tied over the back of the hand. I repaired the deep compartment. 'Remember, any infection travels upwards into the forearm from here,' I said to myself. 'Wash with saline,' a voice from within told me and I did so several times. I darned the deep fascia to cover the tendons and sinews. Were we all under a spell? We continued until the last stitch was in place. Finally, the Sister removed the tourniquet. The pale bloodless hand began to turn pink. There was minimal oozing of blood.

Dr Ahamad looked at the hand and softly whispered his thanks to Allah. The splinting and dressing of the wound were followed by the application of yards of bandaging to immobilise the wrist and fingers. It was eight AM when I moved away and removed my gloves. Three pairs of silent eyes stared at me with a look I could not understand. Did I detect admiration? No one spoke. I thanked Dr Ahamad, the theatre Sister and the nurse. Dr Ahamad was trying to get the patient out of the anaesthetic. The theatre Sister was organising his transfer to the recovery ward. I was beginning to feel that my legs were about to give way. I needed to get out fast and breathe some fresh air.

I tore off the surgical gown and rushed out into the small patch of green in the courtyard, where I was physically sick. The cold morning breeze did soothe and calm me in a little while but when I began to shiver with cold I returned to the duty room. I washed, got dressed, and had a cup of coffee and a cigarette for breakfast.

It was a new day, a new year, a new beginning and 'soon, a new job', I said to myself.

The patient had been admitted to the observation ward by the time I had managed to compose myself. He had come round from the anaesthetic without any problems. The Registrar had taken over and prescribed anti-tetanus shots and intravenous antibiotics. He had managed to get a pint of blood. He saw me and nodded an assurance. I left to attend to other matters on the ward.

Dr Malappa, the Professor, on his afternoon ward round later that day, ordered me to remove the bandages. Dr Ramasamy managed to keep a straight face and said nothing. He had obviously heard of my adventure. I expected to see a mottled black and blue swollen hand ready for amputation. My heart was pounding and my mouth was dry. I could not do it. The Registrar noticed my trembling fingers and stepped forward to help.

The hand had been beautifully darned with hundreds of fine silk sutures. Its shape was perfectly restored. There was no evidence of infection. The last inch of the middle finger had turned blue-black and would not survive but the rest of the hand would heal. The patient could move all his fingers, although with some difficulty and pain. He admitted that he could feel touch on them.

Dr Ramasamy avoided my eyes. The Professor looked at me but said nothing. Smiling, he pointed at me and asked the patient, '*Euruge solpa halu kodtira, amele?*' ('Sir, will you give him some milk, after you get better?') This was the only compliment that I ever received while in surgical training. Perhaps it was a great accolade, coming from the big boss himself.

It was too little and too late.

CHAPTER 2

Some Have Three

I was unemployed during my early days as a doctor. The Health Ministry ran the health services in Nepal, and like all government jobs, vacancies for health professionals were advertised only at certain specified times. The process of appointing doctors was very complicated. One had to follow a strict bureaucratic procedure and observe protocol. New doctors were appointed as Medical Officers after stringent testing by an imposing body of senior civil servants from the Public Service Commission, and formal interviews by the Health Ministry. So, in a country with 280 doctors for ten million people, I was unemployed and likely to remain so for a while. There were no private firms that employed doctors. I had not anticipated this difficulty when I returned home after graduating in India. I had known nothing of these procedures.

The monsoon, a three-month period of incessant rain, had just finished. It was still quite warm and humid that early September morning in Kathmandu when I came across an advertisement in the local newspaper. It was advertising a mobile health camp which was to visit mountainous villages just east of Kathmandu valley. The advert enumerated services such as administering vaccinations to children, dispensing contraceptives, performing vasectomies and inserting intra-uterine contraceptive devices. I was intrigued. This was advertised by a USAID-funded health project called the National Parenthood Foundation (NPF) with headquarters in Kathmandu. I decided to pay them a visit and see if perhaps they needed a doctor.

After giving a series of accounts of myself to the porter, the receptionist, the administrative assistant, the assistant manager and finally the medical officer who was organising the mobile project, I was ushered in to see a young, glamorous woman with a cultivated carefree laugh and flirtatious manner. She was the boss – the CEO of NPF, with an MPH from Harvard University. I began to burble my well-rehearsed story. She was staring at me with great curiosity making me wonder if she had any manners at all. She abruptly interrupted, 'So, you can cut off the vas, can you?' The vas is the tube through which the semen flows out for ejaculation during sexual intercourse.

'I can join it up again too,' I replied promptly. She laughed, tinkling her earrings and leaning backwards on her executive swivel chair so that the *pallo* (the free end of a sari that covers the bosom and shoulder) fell from her shoulder.

'Excellent. I cannot give you employment at the present time but you will be paid per case. The doctor in charge will explain everything to you,' she said, readjusting her *pallo*. I was dismissed.

It was thus that I found myself in a Newar village in Kapcha, a three-day trek from Dhulikhel, the following week. I had formed a team with a nurse, an administrative assistant, a health educator assistant, and four porters carrying supplies. The tour was to last for a month and would take us to at least eight villages. We had been walking since sunrise and the last mile was a steep climb towards the village. It was now sundown and we desperately needed shelter, rest and refreshments. Over the past week we had been shown great hospitality by the poor villagers, grateful for the small services they were receiving. This village appeared different. No curious village children ran to greet us, a practice to which we had become accustomed. People standing in the main village square nodded curtly at us but did not show any welcome.

We reached a small brick building which had corrugated iron sheets for roofing. This was obviously the primary school. The schoolmaster had gone home to the far end of the village. He returned when I sent for him. I wanted his permission to camp in the school, although he did not really have any authority to refuse. I was assumed to be a very senior official from the capital, Kathmandu, able and entitled to demand service!

The attitude of the schoolmaster was rather disturbing. He was distant with us all and appeared uncomfortable at our attempts at joviality. He hastily retreated, saying that the *Pradhan Pancha* (local mayor) would be visiting us soon. In those days, Nepal was under the control of King Mahendra, a ruthless autocrat who had devised an ingenious form of governance called the Panchayat System. There was a *Pradhan Pancha* designated for each small group of villages who was given considerable power over all local affairs. Most of these *Pradhan Panchas* were rogues whose authority came from the patronage of the King or the officials of the Royal Palace, not from any local support.

Our team began to settle down for the evening and I waited for the arrival of the *Pradhan Pancha*. We had to accept his advice on how to run the camp the next day. It was essential that we meet him. Several hours passed before he arrived. He was obviously rich – well dressed with an air of importance about him. I could see his grey hair in spite of the noticeable attempts that had been made to dye it and guessed he was in his mid-sixties. He hid his wrinkles behind the large photochromatic lenses of his spectacles. He was not at all enthusiastic about our camp and was brusque in his manner, making it clear that he did not want any vasectomies to be performed. He was also unwilling to endorse the insertion of Lippes loops (contraceptive devices for the women). All he would agree to was for us to distribute vitamins to the children and pregnant women, and to give vaccinations. He indicated that this should finish by midday and that we should be on our way to the next camp soon after that.

Something was seriously wrong. Why was this village so unhospitable and unwilling? How was I to get to the bottom of this behaviour? We had had a stressful trek to reach it. Besides, each vasectomy was worth twenty rupees to me and I had expected to perform at least six here. All our efforts to reach it were going to be wasted. Something had to be done.

Most male villagers used to gather under a large tree in the centre of the village after their evening meal. They would smoke *tamakhu* (tobacco hookah) and socialise. I decided to join them. I took a few packets of Yak cigarettes which were expensive in the Nepalese context. The brand was filter-tipped and still somewhat novel. One could lightly bite at the filter and look very macho. I also took a bottle of dark rum. It was acceptable to drink alcohol openly there because it was a *Newar Gaon* (village), where most villagers distilled their own *rakshi* (rice spirit). The villages of high caste Brahmins did not allow alcohol to be consumed so publicly.

I could sense the discomfort when I joined the four peasants who were sitting there sharing a hookah. After the customary *namaste* (greeting), I lit a cigarette and passed the packet around. Offering a cigarette is a great ice breaker; sharing a lighted one is a sign of brotherhood. After a little small-talk, I offered a swig from my bottle of rum to the man sitting next to me but did not pass it around. I said that I had heard that the *rakshi* made in that village was the best in the whole of Nepal and I was hoping to taste some before I left. I continued to ask trivial things about the village and let it be known that I might be looking for a local volunteer to help the next day.

When the ice had been broken, I asked innocently why the schoolmaster was so unhelpful. There was an exchange of glances among the group. One of them laughed when he said that the schoolmaster was expecting to have a brother soon. This caused some general merriment and it presented a good opportunity to bring up the topic of vasectomy. No sooner had I mentioned this than there was further laughter and a chorus of, 'No, no, no.'

'I do not want to be like the *Pradhan Pancha*,' said one of the men.

'What happened to the *Pradhan Pancha*?' I enquired.

'His wife is now pregnant,' I was told with much hilarity.

Another packet of cigarettes and several swigs of rum later, I came to know that the schoolmaster was the son of the *Pradhan Pancha*. The *Pradhan Pancha* was very wealthy and most of the villagers owed him money. It was clear that he was not the most popular man in the district. He had undergone a vasectomy but his wife had subsequently become pregnant. He blamed the doctors and the Health Ministry and so had forbidden the villagers to be hospitable to us. At last, I understood what the problem was. Knowing how to solve it was another matter. An idea slowly began to take shape in my mind.

With a straight face, I said that that it must have been a case of three tubes. The villagers looked puzzled but I did not elaborate. The man gulping my rum agreed to present me with a bottle of his best *rakshi* in exchange for the remainder of my bottle. I asked him to bring it the next morning. I offered to pay for the services of two of the men for the work next day and returned to the school. At last I had a strategy.

We set up our stall the next morning. The man who had been drinking my rum was employed to fetch water from the stream at the bottom of the mountain. Another man from the previous evening, who knew how to write, was given the job of registering the children and women. The health educator was taken away from the usual task of registration. I asked him to set up a loud hailer and advised him to repeat the standard spiel about vasectomy periodically. I had also written a notice which was displayed for all the villagers to see. It read: 'Caution is needed in having sexual intercourse after vasectomy because there is still a risk of pregnancy for the first six months. In very rare cases there may be three tubes but only two are cut during standard vasectomy. Sometimes the cut ends can rejoin and become whole once again. Men wanting to have a vasectomy should first consult in detail with the doctor.' Repeated announcement of this cautionary note brought many people to the camp. The *Pradhan Pancha* also came to inspect what we were doing and appeared happier than the previous day. The schoolmaster volunteered to help the nurse with sterilising the syringes and needles.

I could see out of the corner of my eyes that the *Pradhan Pancha* was animatedly talking to a group of male villagers. I was concentrating on screening pregnant women and teaching them how to cut the umbilical cord cleanly to avoid neonatal tetanus. The *Pradhan Pancha* interrupted my work to announce proudly that there were almost a dozen villagers who would like to have a vasectomy done and that we should stay one extra day in the village. With the outward pretence of great reluctance, I eventually agreed after much entreaty by the *Pradhan Pancha*. I was thrilled that my ploy had worked and that I would earn some money after all. Later on in the afternoon, the *Pradhan Pancha* brought his pregnant wife for an examination. His status demanded that I give her VIP treatment. I ushered her into the tent and called the nurse to help me.

She was a beautiful girl, about eighteen years of age, and was pregnant for the first time. The *Pradhan Pancha* had married again last year after his first wife had died. The girl was illiterate and just like any other innocent mountain girl. She was probably the ultimate payment of the debts her father owed to his landlord. I found that she was healthy and her blood pressure was normal. I asked whether she knew that her husband had had a vasectomy. She had no idea about the procedure. She blushed deeply when I explained what vasectomy was and how her husband was no longer capable of fathering a child. I was almost certain that this was not the case of an accessory (third) vas, though such cases do occur. Equally, it did not look likely that the severed vas had rejoined. I gave her the recommended iron and folic acid supplements and explained a few things about pregnancy. Just before going, I advised her that she should have a Lippes loop fitted after her delivery to prevent further pregnancies. She brightened and asked if I would be visiting the village again.

I did happen to do so a few years later to establish a family planning service at the local health post. There was a new schoolmaster who had recently taken up the job. He was a handsome young man and extremely helpful. His predecessor and the *Pradhan Pancha* had had a terrible row soon after our last camp and the former had left the village for good. The *Pradhan Pancha* insisted that I stay with him in his house this time. I was given the best *rakshi* to drink and a *vale* (rooster) was cooked specially for me. A two-year-old boy was playing in the room whose features reminded me of the previous schoolmaster, the *Pradhan Pancha's* son.

His wife served us dinner, giggling all the time. I enjoyed eating the delicacy with my fingers. I do not know what prompted me to ask whether the boy would be educated in the local school in due course. She brightened and said that the school was also being upgraded like the health post and it was very good. Her husband thought that it would be better to teach the boy at home, lest he learn bad manners from the local urchins. The bland expression on his face seemed to imply that he did not trust the schoolmaster. I could not blame him, knowing what I knew.

There were no modern washbasins or running-water taps in homes in those days. One ate with one's fingers and the hostess poured water on one's hands to wash after a meal. Pouring water over my fingers, she asked softly whether the loop could now be fitted at the health post.

CHAPTER 3

Sexual Harassment

How does one investigate a case of alleged rape when there are no witnesses, no medical examination and no evidence? I was once asked to do just that.

'How would you like to represent me and go on a tour of Eastern Nepal?' asked Dr Sugandha Saha, the Chief Executive Officer and wife of the Deputy Prime Minister.

'I would be honoured, of course,' I said.

The rain was lashing down outside at the height of the monsoon season. Clearly, madam was loath to travel under these horrible conditions.

'You will take an accountant, a secretary and my driver,' she instructed. 'Take the new Toyota Land Cruiser which has a multiple re-entry permit to India. Take this file and study the issues. My secretary will brief you as well.' The imperiousness of her orders was appropriate to the bygone feudal times of the Ranas who had been out of power for twenty years.

'Yes, Doctor *saheb*,' I said and got to my feet.

'Have a cup of tea,' she offered, noticing the signs I was taking my leave. The tone of her voice had suddenly softened. I began to feel uncomfortable. She was the boss and a very powerful woman. This was the first time I had been offered a cup of tea in her office, although I had been working temporarily as Chief of the Training Division for over six months. In reality, I was a lowly medical officer.

She hesitated before taking me into her confidence. 'I have found out that the Crown Prince is planning to travel incognito to the eastern districts and will visit many schools and our health posts as well. We have a series of problems in that area which need to be sorted out before he reaches there. I would have gone myself but have to attend the USAID meeting in Washington next week. Dr Nara, the Deputy Chief, is on his annual leave for a month due to some complicated family problems. He cannot be recalled. I have therefore received the approval of the Board for you to go on this trip,' she explained. 'Can you leave tomorrow? The whole trip should not take more than three weeks or so.'

I smiled, trying to appear delighted. 'Of course,' I said, regretting I had not learnt acting in medical school. I just hoped that my demeanour did not reveal my true feelings.

'I will need to submit your report to the Board the day after your return,' she told me. 'Good luck.' I was dismissed.

The file contained a letter authorising me to use executive powers as necessary and was signed by the Chairman of the Board. It felt very good to be considered trustworthy and capable of trouble shooting. The prospect of travelling in the thick of monsoon was, however, daunting as well as exciting in a peculiar sort of way. There were problems at Ilam, Sanischere, Bhadrapur, Dharan, Rajbiraj, Janakpur and Hetaunda. Dr Saha's secretary filled me in on all confidential aspects. I began to study the file and plan my journey.

The East-West highway had not been fully completed. So I planned a series of loops, mainly travelling on the Indian border highways and entering and exiting Nepal from appropriate points. I decided to start from the furthest point in the east and gradually make my way back to Kathmandu. I would go to Darjeeling and reach Pashupatinagar in the Land Cruiser. I would leave the vehicle there and trek to Ilam and

Sanischere on foot. I would have to meet the Zonal Commissioner and other high dignitaries as necessary. I would go to Janakpur and Birgunj last. I was pleased with the prospect of visiting my parents at Janakpur and my elder brother at Birgunj.

I charted the route and dates. The secretary assigned to me was exceedingly competent. He sent telegrams to all these offices informing them of our arrival dates. The directive also cancelled any staff leave and demanded that account books be ready for inspection and internal audit. The driver was a former soldier from the Indian Gurkha regiment, originally from Pokhara. He too was very competent. With the accountant making up the team of four, we set off the next afternoon.

Most of the visits were administrative in nature, although I did also treat a few people. It was in Birajpur that I found I needed to use my clinical skills in a most unusual manner.

We reached Birajpur from Dharan at about four o'clock in the afternoon. The staff of the district headquarters were waiting for us. I greeted all as appropriate and asked the secretary to start making appointments for me to talk to a few of them individually. We found the usual administrative problems such as over expenditure, disparity between supplied and ordered goods, one case of minor insubordination, one allegation of bribery, one act of selling office supplies, and one of alleged sexual harassment.

I decided to tackle the last issue as a priority. One health aide had lodged a formal complaint against the District Officer. It appeared to be a grave accusation but its exact nature was not clear. Health aides are usually female health workers who go from house to house collecting data, dispensing condoms, educating mothers about fluid replacement therapy in diarrhoeal diseases and promoting health education in general. They also need to be members of the local mobile health camp, going from village to village in their district, often spending nights in uncomfortable accommodation. Apparently, the young woman concerned had been molested at night by the District Officer during one of these camps away from the district headquarters.

The District Officer was in his mid-forties, slightly balding and with a protuberant abdomen. He did not know that a complaint had been lodged against him. I asked him to discuss the account books with the accountant. After I had finished with the scheduled appointments, I went to share a glass of sweet tea with the staff during their break. Two of the three health aides, including the complainant, were there. The complainant was in her twenties, provocatively curvaceous with a giggly manner. Did I notice a mild bulge over her lower abdomen? It was well hidden. I continued to talk and joke lightly, and after a while, when the ice had been broken and the staff were leaving to return to their desks, I asked this girl to stay behind and show me the clinic which was located in the adjoining building.

No-one would hear us there and no-one would suspect that I was actually investigating her complaint. She blushed scarlet and appeared frightened when she found that I knew of her grievance. I asked her to detail the exact circumstances of the harassment. She burst into tears. Between sobs, she told me that when she had gone out at night from the hut in which all the staff had camped, the DO had caught her by surprise. He had taken her behind a hay stack and actually had sexual intercourse with her. She had protested but he would not stop. He was strong and she could smell the alcohol on his breath. He would not let her go. He promised her promotion and offered many trips away from home which would bring her additional income. She was terrified but could not raise her voice and so she had submitted in silence.

She swore that intercourse had occurred. There were no witnesses. At first she did not know what to do and felt unable to confide in anyone. Finally, she had gathered sufficient courage to write directly to the CEO who, being a woman herself, would understand, she hoped.

I let her go but said that I would be talking to her again. She touched my feet in deference and left the room, weeping. This was more serious than I had thought. The allegation was of rape. I had to determine whether or not I could trust her story. Was she telling me the truth? Why would she lie?

The DO had made arrangements for me to stay with him in his house. I politely declined and checked into a hotel which was not very comfortable. I accepted a dinner invitation, however. It would have been very discourteous to refuse. Also, I hoped that he would be off guard in his own home which might give me some insight into his character. I was uncomfortable at the prospect of accepting his hospitality whilst investigating him at the same time.

His wife greeted me at the door that evening. She was in her late thirties and was the head of the history department at the local college. The DO offered me a Scotch whisky but took only a glass of water for himself. He had been a diabetic for over twenty-five years. He had given up alcohol about two years earlier when he had started to have problems with his vision. He had been found to have high levels of cholesterol and had had to go to India for laser treatment on his eyes. The couple appeared to have resigned themselves to his ill health. Luckily they had no children, he told me, looking sad. I looked at his wife. She was quite attractive and looked young for a departmental head. The couple appeared devoted to each other. They were cultured and obviously maintained high standards for themselves. Why would a man behave so badly with a member of the junior staff?

The evening went on quite pleasantly. I had recently returned from an educational tour of USA and told them interesting stories about this trip. I remember telling them of my visit to a nightclub in San Francisco which was actually a sex clinic run by the local catholic priest. He would teach the men about safe sex and also treat all kinds of sexual problems, including impotence. The couple were fascinated by this story. Was I mistaken? Did I actually notice a glance that passed between the wife and husband when I mentioned impotence?

Birajpur hospital had been without a doctor for several weeks. The DO was on medication for hypertension and had not had a check-up recently. I offered to check his blood pressure and to give him a full physical examination the following morning, if he wished. He was relieved and his wife was positively grateful. I thanked my generous hosts and bade them good night.

The next day, I checked the DO's blood pressure and examined him in detail. I found that he had peripheral neuropathy with greatly reduced ability to feel pain in response to touch and pinprick tests in his feet and legs. He was showing many signs of diabetic complications, including impairment of the functions controlled by his autonomic nervous system. He had no idea what I was doing. Although I could not ask him about any sexual symptoms, I became pretty well convinced that he was impotent. If so, he could not have had sexual intercourse with the Health Aide. So why was he being accused of rape?

The DO would not tell me of any problems with his staff. He had a protective attitude towards them; they in turn seemed to think highly of him. The accountant had looked at the books and found everything in order. The person stealing the office supplies had been dismissed.

During my informal chat with the other health aide, I came to know that the complainant had been the thief who stole the supplies. She had been appointed as a health aide three months after the incident. The DO was so good to the staff that he had given her the new job after sacking her as an office assistant. She had begged, cried and said that her parents were old and ill, that the whole family would suffer if she did not get a job. She had sworn not to steal ever again. After several weeks, the DO had been appeased and given her the job.

The plot was thickening. Why would she lodge a complaint against her own benefactor? Did the man just want to have some gratification even though he was unlikely to be able to penetrate her sexually?

Later that day I called for her again. I decided to gamble on calling her bluff. I boldly told her that the DO had advanced diabetes and that people in that state could not perform sexual intercourse. So, she must have lied. I would call the police and have her arrested unless she told me the truth.

She broke down once again and denied that she had been lying. I then told her that she was also a thief and had been caught red handed. I was not moved by her histrionics. I did not budge although it was difficult at times not to be fooled by her superb acting. Finally she saw she was not getting anywhere with this approach and agreed to confess if I promised not to call the police. I did not promise this but agreed to give her a fair hearing.

I could see that she was struggling to tell the truth and had to encourage her. Finally, she blurted out that the DO had caught her having sexual intercourse with a man in the clinic room. She had bluffed that he was her fiancé. The DO had laughed and told her to be careful. He had not taken any action against her.

'So why accuse the DO?' I asked. She explained that her lover had given her some money and then vanished. She had found subsequently that she had missed her period. Knowing that she was in trouble she had somehow to explain the pregnancy whilst preserving her reputation within the community. Unmarried women were not supposed to get pregnant in those days. She had decided that implicating the DO was her only option.

She had been able to manipulate him once before and had got her job back. She hoped that she would be able successfully to manipulate the story of his kindness. She would say that she could not deny her benefactor. This way, she would not lose face in her community. I was relieved to know the truth at last. I asked her to write two letters; one withdrawing her allegations, the other resigning with immediate effect.

I handed that letter of resignation to the DO the next day. He was puzzled. He muttered something about how irresponsible people could be, quitting their jobs without giving any reason or proper period of notice.

CHAPTER 4

My First Helicopter Ride

'How would you like to establish three new clinics in Bara, Parsa and Rautahat, one in each district?' asked the CEO. It was obviously an order but given in a very polite manner, which was not at all usual for her. I could sense that something was not right.

'I should be delighted, of course. When?' I enquired hastily, hoping to avoid the trip in the thick of the monsoon. 'It will be difficult to leave Kathmandu for several days at this busy time. There is no one else to teach the new batch of Health Aides. Besides, the seminar for the Medical Officers and the workshop for the District Officers (DOs) are scheduled for next week.'

The workshop and seminar were important events where our distinguished CEO was also going to speak. Both were high-profile events, which I had arranged and publicised. They were going to be attended by the Chief of USAID, our donor, and advisors and international observers. Our training budget for the next year was at stake.

There was a little silence. 'Can you spare just one day, please?' she asked sweetly. It was clear that she had already thought of a way.

'Yes, but can we cover three districts in one day?' My incredulity must have shown. She laughed the tinkling laugh for which she was famous.

She threw back her head and replaced the fallen delicate sari over her bosom. 'A helicopter will be waiting at the airport tomorrow morning at seven.' She smiled triumphantly. 'Harry will pick you up as he lives close to your house. There are files for you to study tonight. There will be a DO in each of those locations. You will be representing the CEO. You should be back by the end of the day.'

Her personal assistant handed me the files and a letter of authority. She turned to him. 'Get Harry on the phone. Tell him it is very important,' she instructed. 'Contact Everest (the helicopter company) and book the four-seater from seven AM. If necessary, ask them to cancel the previous bookings. Tell them that it has become necessary to do so because of *Rashtria Panchayat* (Parliament) business. They can contact me personally if there are any problems.'

Such was the nature of our CEO. She was decisive, a problem solver and was highly influential because she was also the wife of a friend of King Birendra. Nobody would dare to deny her simple request to hire a helicopter.

I knew that the budget for the helicopter hire would be met by USAID if one of the US advisors travelled in it. Hence Harry Youngman was to be contacted. He would be delighted to help out because it was his remit to advise on health education. The other seat was for the project photographer.

I thanked her and returned to my office. I had to readjust the teaching schedule for the next day. Reading through the files it became clear that these clinics should have been established a year earlier. Several dates for the openings had been set and then postponed for a variety of reasons. The CEO had somehow discovered that the Honourable Members from Bara, Parsa and Rautahat, unhappy with the delay, were planning to table a motion at the next *Rastria Panchayat* session, which would have made the Health Minister feel uncomfortable. They were going to demand an explanation as to why the promised clinics had not been established. The local villagers desperately needed maternal and child health services and contraception. The people were suffering and now that the monsoon was at its worst, the women could not even reach the district headquarters for treatment. The House was scheduled to debate this issue two days later. Hence it was necessary to establish the clinics before this could happen. She would avoid the blame and the Health Minister would score a point. She was very clever.

I did feel a sense of adventure. I had never been in a helicopter before and this was an experience I longed to have. Harry picked me up as expected at six-thirty AM. We went to the helipad via the VIP entrance, thanks to Harry's Land Cruiser with diplomatic number plates and a uniformed chauffer. The helicopter was ready for us. The pilot, a beefy Texan with an irritatingly brusque manner, checked his records. We were to go to Rampur in Parsa, Lachmania in Bara, and Chandranigahapur in Rautahat. We lifted off at seven AM. The photographer was late and the pilot would not wait even a few minutes for him. Luckily, Harry had brought his expensive Leica.

The rain had stopped earlier and it was a bright sunny morning. The lush vegetation over the huge mountains looked beautiful. We had to climb up to nine thousand feet to get out of the valley, over the pass at the south-west corner. Soon we were over Chitwan and then came Parsa, which looked like a huge lake. I was amazed when the pilot landed us on a small stretch of dry tarmac close to a hut, the site for the proposed clinic.

The District Officer was waiting for us. Over hot *poori* (fried bread), *tarkari* (vegetable curry), omelette and sweet tea, we had our breakfast meeting. The pilot grimaced at our invitation to breakfast and sauntered off to the cockpit to munch on a stick of salami. The official opening was scheduled for ten o'clock that morning. I suggested that the local *Pradhan Pancha* (mayor) should inaugurate the clinic by cutting a red rope, as there was no ribbon. At the chosen moment he duly did so and gave a short speech. I followed his lead and also said a few words. Subsequently, I inoculated several babies, examined some pregnant mothers, dispensed multivitamin and iron tablets and distributed a lot of condoms. All these activities were duly photographed by Harry. We took off at eleven-thirty AM. One done, two more to go.

The same process was repeated at Lachmania. We did not stop to have lunch. We lifted off at one-thirty PM to go to Chandranigahapur to establish the third clinic. Our plan was to finish the job by half past three so that we could avoid the bad weather forecast for the late afternoon. The formalities of opening the last clinic being over, I was giving away the last of the condoms when a bullock cart appeared as if from nowhere. The village midwife explained to me that a woman pregnant with her fourth child had gone into labour that morning and she had been summoned to conduct the delivery. The mother of three had pushed the feet of the baby out first. The midwife had tried to pull the baby out but could not do so. The shoulder had got stuck and the patient was getting exhausted. The midwife knew that the clinic was to be inaugurated that day and so had brought the patient for expert treatment.

It was three PM. I had seen one breech delivery two years earlier when I was writing up the required twenty cases for our obstetrics course. The registrar had applied forceps to deliver the baby. I had read about breech presentations and had memorised the answers to a few standard questions that were likely to be asked in the viva examination. This was all very different. There were no forceps to apply, nor the expertise to conduct the procedure. I was expected to do something to help this poor woman and child. I prayed silently.

I looked around to see the helicopter resting nearby. I boldly approached the pilot and asked him to take us and the pregnant woman to Birgunj hospital, fifty miles away. There were trained obstetricians and gynaecologists there. To my utter vexation, he flatly refused. He was not authorised to allow any passenger that was not mentioned in his records. He did not seem to care if the woman died. 'Not my problem,' he said openly and continued to chew gum, totally indifferent. How I hated the man!

It was down to me. I explained to Harry that I might have to delay our departure a little and that he should keep the pilot on hold. He must not take off without me or else his company would never fly in Nepal again. My fury was masking my apprehension and lack of confidence. All the gathered villagers were looking at me expectantly. The patient herself must have had great hopes too. Taking a deep breath, I asked for her to be taken inside the building. Our Health Aide brought fresh towels and lit a paraffin lantern so that I could inspect the patient.

She was about twenty-four years old and had a good, fit body. Her pulse was a little fast but strong and regular. Her blood pressure was normal. I put her in the standard 'lithotomy' position – lying on her back, legs lifted up, knees bent and thighs separated – and examined her. The two lower limbs had come out and the baby's buttocks were visible at the vulval opening. I held the legs with a towel for better grip and tried to pull gently. The baby was stuck.

'Don't panic. Be methodical. Try to remember all that you learned in the past,' I murmured under my breath. I had to make the opening wider and so performed an episiotomy (a cut to enlarge the opening of the birth canal). A name tried to rise from the deepest recesses of my brain. Mauriceau's manoeuvre. A famous mime artist had a similar name!

But that was to deliver a stuck head. I could not remember what to do for the shoulder.

I pushed my hand in and began to feel and identify the parts of the baby. The baby was lying flat on its back. I tried rotating it gently, remembering something about the antero-posterior diameter of the shoulders. This was successful. I could now see the shoulder blade and a few lower ribs. Some hope at last. I continued to pull gently. The other shoulder also came out spontaneously. Now the head was stuck. I rotated it again slowly but this made no difference.

Then I remembered Dr Kamalamma, our professor, telling us never to put pressure on the baby's jaw with our finger inside its mouth as this could break its neck. I shuddered at the prospect. Then the sketch of Mauriceau's manoeuvre swam before my eyes. I tried to visualise the diagram in my head as clearly as I could. I put my index finger into the baby's mouth gently and manipulated the baby's body, making it rest upon my forearm. Then, pressing upon the mother's abdomen with my free hand, I slowly lifted my forearm (which was supporting the baby) upwards to one side. There was a little give. So I asked the Health Aide to apply the pressure while I maintained the baby in the same position inside the womb and pulled its legs. Seemingly miraculously, this push and pull brought the head out. We had done it! The woman breathed a huge sigh of relief. She had two reasons to feel good. Her life had been saved and she had produced a son after three daughters. Luckily, it did not take long for the placenta (afterbirth) to come out. I sewed the episiotomy and asked the Health Aide and the village midwife to take over. The baby did not look premature and cried with a full pair of lungs. I hurried to the waiting helicopter. It was already near six PM.

Harry was most impressed. He had not witnessed even a normal delivery before. Seeing an incomplete breech expertly delivered in the most primitive conditions was unbelievable for him. He kept on ahh-ing and ooh-ing and asking me a multitude of questions in his excitement. The pilot was deafeningly silent and glared at me ferociously. But I was too exhausted to care.

Five minutes later we were enveloped in dark clouds. The pilot tried to gain height in an attempt to escape but was rewarded with sheeting rain and wind. We were pushed miles off course and lost radio contact. We flew for another ten minutes, each suspecting that this was our last flight alive. Ten more minutes and we briefly glimpsed the vegetation of a huge mountain ahead. The pilot turned sharply to avoid the collision.

I asked if he could climb to thirteen thousand feet. The tallest peak in the Mahabharat range of the mountains is just above twelve thousand. 'Then you will have radio contact,' I said.

'I have nearly run out of fuel,' he hissed at me with cold fury. It was my fault, he was absolutely sure. He continued, 'The bloody woman was not your f***ing problem. You were sent to open clinics, not deliver babies. Now all of us are going to die on this godforsaken mountain. F*** you. I will kill you first before I die.'

It was cold in the cabin. Harry had turned white and perspiration was matting his thick beard. He could not speak. I still remember those terror-stricken eyes. It had been a most adventurous day for him. He had seen the beginning of life and was now glimpsing his own death. Only a soft moan was audible coming from somewhere deep inside him.

I remembered Leela and Nandan, both asleep at six that morning. They will never see me again, I thought. I wondered if I would be able to see them as a ghost. I was in a most indifferent state of mind as though my brain had become incapable of any other thought or emotion. I was staring into the darkness all around me. Then I saw it. I grabbed the pilot's shoulder and pointed to the spot in the distance. He saw it before it vanished from our sight.

He made another sharp turn and headed towards the patch of cornfield. It was a relatively flat space on the top of a small mountain. The patch was barely fifteen feet wide and twenty feet long. It was covered with maize saplings. The helicopter landed there without any ceremony. The pilot switched off the engine and remained fixed to his seat. Harry and I crawled from the cabin and looked at each other in disbelief. We hugged, sobbing with relief. Once composed, ashamed of admitting our own weaknesses, we began to talk as if nothing had happened.

'There must be a *goth* (animal shed) near here,' I said looking around, after realising that I had landed on a pile of cow dung. Then we heard voices in the distance. Villagers had noticed the light of the helicopter in that bad weather and seen that it had practically fallen from the sky. They had come to see the accident. They took us to a nearby *pati* (bothy). People continued to come in despite the rain and darkness. They brought *cheura* (rice flakes) and *chang* (home brew from millet). Someone had a *madal* (drum), another had a harmonica. We spent the night munching *cheura*, drinking *chang* and joining in the spontaneous limericks – for us, the most beautiful songs of survival that anybody had ever sung. At first we did not notice that the pilot was not with us. Harry went to talk to him but he refused to leave the aircraft. He was not authorised to do so it apparently. The insurance conditions would have been breached.

It was nearly four in the morning when most of us were exhausted into sleep. We were awoken with a start by the loud noise of the helicopter. The pilot had decided to take advantage of the clear dawn to fly into Kathmandu. He would have left us there sleeping if we had not hurried. He flew us straight up and we could see that we were over the pass at the south-east corner of the valley, about fifty miles from the pass in the south-western corner that we had been aiming for. We entered the valley and landed at a field in Thimi, about five miles from the airport, which would not open until six AM. Harry was allowed to use the radio in the chopper. He asked the night duty officer at USAID to send a car to pick us up as soon as possible. The pilot would be delayed there because he had made an unauthorised landing.

It was seven AM when I reached home. Nandan came running to greet me and made a face. 'You smell awful, Daddy,' he said and went to wake his mother.

PART II

A Medical Officer In Rural Nepal

SECTION I
Jumla

CHAPTER 5

I Will Need To Break Your Other Leg

The controller of postal services had fallen from a *lisno* (ladder), breaking his leg. That was three days earlier in the distant district of Mugu. The villagers had wrapped his broken leg in the wide leaves of the *Sal* tree, splinted on four sides with bamboo sticks. They had covered it with molten molasses and gum latex, *khoto,* which had soon set into a hard casing on exposure to the cold wind. He could bear very little weight, even when aided by a makeshift shoulder crutch and with copious amounts of *rakshi* (local beer) to mask the pain. He had travelled to my hospital on the back of a skinny pony, with two peons supporting him on either side. As a controller of postal services covering four districts, he had to travel extensively. Inspections, quality checks and security testing were three of the many aspects of his job that only he could do. He was a big man in his late thirties, married with no children. His wife was a pretty young woman who kept house for him and did not accompany him on his tours. I had met him and his wife a few times, socially.

It was a bitterly cold January afternoon. The remote, mountainous Karnali region of western Nepal was frozen. The snow of late December to early January does not melt until late March. The average daytime temperature of minus five degrees Celsius drops to minus twelve or thirteen at night. The trails, frozen hard with ice, some wide, others narrow and all invariably slippery, need great caution to negotiate. I knew how perilous it was to walk in those conditions. Every step carried the risk of plunging thousands of feet down the steep slopes of those gigantic mountains. When such incidents occur, it is sometimes impossible to retrieve the body. My latest patient had perhaps been lucky.

I took him to the examination-cum-treatment room. It was basic; without electricity, heating or running water. A kerosene heater struggled to provide warmth. Mr Postal Service was a little tipsy. A combination of *bhang* (marijuana) and *rakshi* had evidently dulled his inhibitions as well as his pain.

'If that bitch had given me a chamber pot, my leg would not have been broken,' he began to rant. 'Wait till I lay my hands on her.' Mita, my nurse, and I looked at each other. The afternoon would perhaps bring some entertainment, after all. He peered at me. 'She is the best. That's why I go to her. Bitch, you just wait.'

We got on with our job. His trousers needed to be cut open, a difficult task due to his makeshift cast. He fainted with pain on one occasion because I did not dare to give him any morphine, pethidine or even a quick whiff of ether on top of the alcohol he had drunk. He had sustained fractures of both the tibia and fibula of his right leg. The tibia appeared to have been broken in two places. In addition, there was an enormous bruise over the right thigh. This had not been strapped, probably remaining unnoticed by the villagers. The grating of the fractured ends of the femur (the long bone in the thigh) was unmistakable. This made Mr Postal Service utter a profound expletive and poor Mita turned crimson with embarrassment.

I needed to ascertain the extent of bleeding and damage to major arteries and veins. I could feel the popliteal artery behind his knee and the one that runs over the foot – the *dorsalis pedis*. I pricked him with a pin at various points in the lower limb. He cursed each time, telling me that his nerves were intact. His foot had not mottled blue or turned cold which suggested that the blood supply was also undamaged.

He was a heavy man with large thighs. He needed proper manipulation and fixation of the broken femur ends. He needed x-rays. He needed an orthopaedic surgeon. But there was none. There was only me, who had never before treated a fracture of the femur, nor multiple fractures of the tibia.

Clearly something had to be done, but what would be appropriate? The man was dehydrated and drowsy. Thankfully, the skin over the broken bones was intact. His pulse was rapid. He had a mild fever, probably resulting from extensive tissue necrosis.

'How the hell am I going to treat him?' I asked myself loudly. Mita was startled.

Back to basics; start with first aid. I set up an intravenous drip of dextrose saline infusion to correct his dehydration. What next? I looked into our meagre medicine cupboard and found some indomethacin. This is a very nasty drug, which can perforate the stomach or bowel, destroy blood cells and make you bleed if taken for long. However, it is a very potent anti-inflammatory agent and also reduces pain. I crushed two tablets into a fine powder, blended with milk, added generous heaps of sugar and made him swallow the mixture.

I then had to immobilise the leg and manipulate and fix the fractures. It was clearly not possible to do this immediately. So I put long strips of sticking plaster on either side from the top of the thigh to the sole of the foot and securely stuck the lower ends together. I covered the leg with loose gauze pieces. I hoped he would sleep well that night. Nature is the biggest healer and I felt I would have thought of something by the next morning. Mrs Postal Service had arrived by this time and cowered in a corner. I tried to reassure her, all the while conscious of the severe doubt in my own voice.

I had reduced the angle of breakage for simple fractures and applied plaster casts before, mostly in children. I had no book on orthopaedics and found no guidance in *Harrison's Textbook of Medicine*, normally my bible and constant companion.

I was worried. Would the leg survive? Would it be deformed to the extent that the man would require crutches for the rest of his life? Would it be possible to do a reasonably good job of manipulation and immobilisation without an x-ray and orthopaedic expertise? If so, how?

As darkness fell I went to my house and mulled over the problem. I returned a few hours later to find Mr Postal Service fast asleep, looking much less troubled. His pulse was steady and strong. I left for my own bed, hoping for some divine inspiration in my sleep so that I could fix the bones the next day.

I saw Mr Postal Service the following morning. He had had a good sleep. He had woken up early and was hungry. His wife had already fed him *puri, tarkari* and *tareko ful* and *baklo dudh* (fried unleavened bread, potato fries, fried eggs, and sugared and thickened buffalo milk). After this heavy meal, it would be inadvisable to administer general anaesthesia so fracture reduction in this manner was not an option. He was shocked to learn that he had broken his thigh bone as well as his shin. Although rather hazy about events following the fall, he gave a good general account of what had happened.

It had been a particularly successful tour of Humla. He was on his way back to Jumla and had reached the foothills of Danfe lek at dusk, tired and hungry. He would not be able to cross the mountain that night to reach Jumla on the other side. The pass itself was at seventeen thousand feet. So he had taken a little detour. He had arrived at the house of Kanchi Kathini in Mugu and asked for shelter for the night.

Most of houses in those villages were hardly better than mud huts. The ground floor would be occupied by the cattle. The family would sleep around a fire pit on the first floor. The top of the roof would have a hole to allow the smoke to escape. The thick sticky smoke of the Himalayan pine with its distinctive smell would cling to you for days. Most hosts would allow guests to sleep in a corner of their parlour just outside the main room. Others would let them come into the warm smoke-filled room. The houses did not have stairs but used carved tree trunks as ladders. These were known as *lisno*. With no banister for support, one needed to be sure-footed to go up and down these steps.

Kanchi Kathini was young, beautiful, and lonely. Her husband had been absconding for several months. She had good tastes and standards. She would only oblige officers on tours and clean-looking tourists. Not only would they get shelter for the night; she would cook a rooster and rice and serve her best *rakshi* with the meal. Whether they would be allowed to share her bed would depend upon how much they were prepared to spend. She would give a discount for regular and generous customers like our controller, of course.

The controller continued his story. It had been a most satisfactory experience for him. Kanchi had obliged his every request. Then, during the night, he had needed to urinate. It was very cold outside and gently snowing. He asked for a chamber pot but she said that it was outside. She did not wish to get dressed to go and fetch it. She suggested that he might as well go out into the bushes. So he was forced to get up and go out into the night. He had not been amused and decided that she owed him one more session as punishment. He was returning to her, on the third step of the *lisno,* when a huge dog jumped at him, barking ferociously. He fell onto hard ice, hurt his leg, slipped downhill twenty yards and hit his thigh on a rock. He could not get up. The continued barking alerted the neighbours who lifted and bandaged him. They gave him more *rakshi* and a smoke of *ganja* for good measure to relieve the pain.

These ferocious dogs were the guard dogs, locally known as *Bhote Kukur* (Tibetan mastiffs). The villagers keep them chained during the day when they appear mostly asleep and harmless. The master of the house sets them loose just before retiring at night. The dogs then seem to come to life and patrol the whole village, barking at any sound or movement. Their barks can be heard over large areas. These dogs not only keep thieves away; they frighten away night-time predators like cheetah, other wild cats, wolves and jackals from entering the village. It came as no surprise that my patient had been attacked by a dog.

I removed his bed clothes and the gauze bandages. The whole leg was tinged blue. My initial alarm ceased when I noted that the limb was warm, with good blood flow and sense of touch. Obviously the haematoma (bruise) had spread all along the subcutaneous layer. Thankfully, the swelling over his thigh had also reduced a little. I explained that a very tricky manoeuvre was required and I would need his full cooperation if the leg was to be saved. He agreed; what else could he do? I gave him another 100 mg of indomethacin and promised to return in an hour or so to set the bones. I spent that hour doing routine chores and desperately trying to figure out a way to do the job properly.

On my return, I got him lifted onto a hard table in the centre of the room. I spread sheets of gauze and rolls of cotton wool under the broken thigh. The first step was to stretch his leg as much as possible. Two big orderlies from above and two others from below pulled him in opposite directions. Both his legs had to be pulled, otherwise his pelvis would tilt and the manoeuvre would fail. The adhesive plaster from the day before helped to align the broken leg in an anatomical manner. Mita was holding on to this with both hands. The patient screamed at first with the choicest obscenities but became suddenly quiet. I was tracing the vague contour of the femur from the inner surface of the thigh and at that point, it felt as though the two ends of the bone had 'approximated' (lined up). The patient had not fainted but the sharp pain had vanished from his thigh. This was my chance to tie the bandages loosely so that Mita would now be able to hold the thigh from both sides and keep the approximation in alignment. The orderlies were maintaining the same pull and doing a great job as witnessed by beads of perspiration on their foreheads and red faces.

I now turned my attention to the lower leg. I decided to ignore the fractured fibula because I could not feel it except just underneath the knee. I began to trace the ridge of bone over the shin, signalling the orderly pulling at it to alter the direction as necessary. The upper end was easy to follow but the bones at the lower fracture site were difficult to define. I had to estimate their direction of lie by comparison with the good leg. Painstakingly and slowly, the manipulations continued. I felt that the best fix had been achieved under the circumstances. Two other orderlies were now needed to assist with my first application of a full limb plaster cast. Eight of us had to be actively involved in these manoeuvres. I hoped that that would be the last. At the end of it all, my patient was able to wiggle his toes and was no longer swearing obscenities.

I kept him in hospital for the rest of that day. His wife brought him specially prepared rooster with rice. I advised her to feed him very little of it and to give him less rich food like soups and fluids instead. She was disappointed at this suggestion. 'What shall I do with this then?' she asked. 'I am sure we can help you dispose of it,' I said with a straight face. We had not had rooster for many weeks. It was indeed very tasty.

Mr Postal Service did well over the next twenty-four hours. He had only mild pain and started to talk normally. He was fearful about whether his leg would heal. I explained that he would need to be on total bed rest for two weeks to help the swelling subside. The plaster would need to be changed after that.

I discharged him to his own house with strict instructions not to get up or walk, to use bed pans and urine bottles, to continue to wiggle his toes several times during the day, and strictly to avoid alcohol. I felt that the last dictum was justified in case he drank one too many and forgot my other instructions. Over the next two weeks, I visited him a few times at his house. All was going well. On removing the cast I was pleased to see that the swelling had gone down. The thigh also had considerably reduced in bulk due to muscle wasting through disuse. The limb looked like it was properly aligned. I applied a fresh cast and reinforced the heel so that he could now start to walk a little with crutches.

Feeling very pleased with myself, I returned home that evening. A generous swig of rum with hot black tea seemed just the right thing to have before retiring for the frozen night. Much later I was awoken by pounding at our front door. Someone had come to call me urgently to the patient's house. Apparently, he was in pain and cursing everyone. His wife was distressed and crying despairingly

I hurried to the house, carrying my bag as usual, accompanied by the orderly on duty. The situation was very much as I had been told. Mrs Postal Service was in one corner, wailing and cursing herself. She rushed at me and flung herself at my feet, begging my forgiveness for having given him a drink.

The *rakshi* was getting the blame for the excruciating pain in his thigh. I cut away parts of the plaster to find that the bones had been displaced. I did not believe that the *rakshi* was the direct cause. He must have moved very forcefully. I had to take him back to the hospital. The eight of us were now an experienced team, working together as though we had been doing this job all our lives. The broken femoral ends were approximately aligned once again and the plaster was reapplied. The whole cycle had to be repeated. I hoped that the fractured ends had lined up well this time; it was difficult in the presence of scar tissue and bruising. I was prepared for a little shortening of the limb.

When I applied the walking cast for the second time two further weeks later, I asked the lady of the house not to give her husband any *rakshi* again. I also asked Mr Postal Service not to indulge in any mischief. She blushed and hurriedly retreated from the room. Her husband smiled ruefully and decided to confess.

That day, as usual, he had eaten his evening meal. He had felt fine. He had taken a few easy steps with his crutches earlier. He had been able to sit on a stool, which had felt good. He had not had any alcohol for all that time and had thought that one drop would not hurt him. He had had no sex either during all these weeks. The thought of Kanchi Kathini and her *rakshi* had come fresh to his mind. His wife had looked more desirable than ever. Lying on his bed, face up, he had found that he was aroused. He had called his wife, who had declined to do anything for him.

He had woken up two hours later, after a vivid erotic dream. So he had asked her merely to squat over his thighs whilst he remained passive. All went fine. His wife had begun to relax a little and he to get his confidence. They had been about to explode into the greatest ecstasy when he had heard a loud 'crack'; it was the snap of his femur, making him curse and scream loudly. At first his wife thought that she had greatly pleased her husband but within an instant knew that that was not the cause of his expletives. I struggled to stifle my laughter. I cautioned him again. He promised to behave. It took ten weeks altogether for him to walk again.

The entire staff of our hospital was present when I eventually removed the cast. The first thing I noticed was how much the bulk of the thigh muscles had shrunk. There was also a convex hard swelling of bony scar tissue over the broken ends of the femur. The tibia had healed beautifully. There was a hard swelling deep and lateral to the gastrocnemius muscle (the bulky muscle on the back of the leg) in his calf. When the patient stood up he had to tilt his pelvis. I measured his legs and found that the right was now shorter by an inch. Mr Postal Service was disappointed with the result. He began to limp a little when he walked. I advised him to get a shoe raise and said that I would instruct the local cobbler to make one. This made him furious.

He accused me of being the worst quack he had come across in his life. How dare I call myself a doctor? He hoped that a similar quack would treat me as well when I broke my leg, as surely God would make that happen to punish me. His wife did not say a word but looked at me with tears in her eyes. Why tears? Was she sorry for her husband or for herself for having a husband like him? He would go to Kathmandu the next day and show his leg to the best specialist there. He demanded a letter of referral, with which I obliged. My staff were outraged. They knew how hard we had all worked to save that leg. We had never been so insulted. A few of the orderlies were making fists. I had to look at them sternly so they would control themselves. Mr Postal Service limped away with his wife in tow. Our hopes had been dashed and we no longer felt like celebrating.

Several weeks passed after this incident. It was the weekly plane day, the day that the twenty-seat airplane would land on the grass airfield in Jumla. Hundreds of people would be there to watch its arrival. Letters, fresh vegetables, and new people would arrive and we would all feel some connection with the outside world. It was the end of *Chaitra*, the last month in the Nepalese calendar. Leela and I had been promised a transfer to Kathmandu in the New Year. I was eagerly awaiting a letter from the Department of Health informing us that we had indeed been relocated.

There was nothing for us. Disappointed, I was about to return when I saw Mr Postal Service pointing at his luggage to be picked up by a porter. I hid myself among the crowd to avoid meeting him. I could see that he was walking almost normally, although he was carrying a cane. I became busy with other things and forgot all about him.

Early the next morning I was sitting in my garden when Mr Postal Service came to the house. He was very polite. He did his *namaste* and remained standing until I asked him to sit down. After preliminary greetings, he informed me that he had gone to see Dr Agni Sharma, the most renowned orthopaedic consultant in Kathmandu. He had had to pay hefty fees and bribe his secretary for an early appointment. Dr Sharma had x-rayed his thigh and leg. Instead of sympathising with him, Dr Sharma had rebuked him for wasting his time. 'Dr Gautam has done a first-class job on you yet you are not satisfied. I could not have done any better under those circumstances. You owe him an apology,' he had said. When Mr Postal Service had complained about the shortened limb, Dr Sharma had merely shrugged and said 'Then I will need to break your other leg. Only that way can I make them equal.' The shoe raise suddenly seemed more attractive.

He said all this sheepishly. He had brought fresh spinach from Kathmandu and a bottle of rum as a present for me. I promised to share the drink with the staff.

Just before leaving, he apologised again and brightly suggested that I join him on a trip to Mugu that weekend. His meaning was obvious. 'No, thank you,' I said. 'I do not want to break my leg.' We both laughed and the sun came out of the clouds.

CHAPTER 6

Let The Water Out

Nandan, our son, was being held upon the back of a pony by Sante, one of the hospital porters. The three-year-old was very excited by the prospect of riding around the hospital compound, yet the pony did not appear to share his pleasure and was bucking in protest. Two strangers were also part of the scene. They had evidently brought the pony to the hospital and were encouraging my son merrily.

'Get the child off at once,' I shouted to no-one in particular. I had returned to the hospital to be greeted by a sight which I did not like. My order was immediately obeyed and Nandan ran towards me with expectation in his eyes. I picked him up and looked questioningly at the two villagers. '*Namaste, saheb,*' both said, bending deeply from the waist in obeisance.

They had brought the pony to carry me to Tatopani. The community leader there had been unable to urinate for two days and was in agony. He could not be brought to the hospital, they explained, because he was in his father's *kiria*. I knew that this was serious. *Kiria* is a period of mourning the dead. The son must light the funeral pyre of his parent and return to observe *kiria*. During this time he should not be touched by anyone because that would defile him. He can wear only one *dhoti* (a single sheet of cotton to wrap around the body) and cover himself with only one blanket. He must sleep on the floor on a small mat or pile of hay and eat just one meal each day. He is not allowed to smoke, drink alcohol, eat meat or add salt to food. He must live near running water so that he can perform daily ablutions there. He must pray and do some *pooja* (a religious ritual) according to the instructions of his family priest. His wife has to cook the small meal, usually a bowl of rice with some green vegetables flavoured with the minimum of spices and without salt. After this meagre meal, he must receive the villagers, other friends and relatives and listen to religious stories from the *Puranas* (religious texts describing the journey of a spirit). This routine lasts for twelve days. On the thirteenth day, he must take a purifying bath, do a proper *shraddha* (ritual offering of rice balls cooked in milk to the spirit of the parent and all ancestors) and invite all the relatives for a celebratory feast in the name of the departed parent. That ends the mourning period officially.

'How many days?' I asked.

'Three,' they said. He had been unable to pass urine since cremating his father's body three days earlier.

I had no choice. One did not demur and make excuses, especially at times of death. It mattered little that Tatopani was more than twelve miles away. The villagers had brought the pony to help with the arduous four-hour trek over mountainous terrain. I had not visited that area before. I explained the nature of this house call to Leela, my wife. She understood the urgency and gravity of the situation and agreed to cancel whatever we had planned for that day. I hoped to be back by the evening.

I hurried with the preparations. I gathered my doctor's bag and made sure it contained a few urinary catheters, a tub of petroleum jelly, sterilised syringes, needles, cotton swabs, bandages and surgical gloves. I also checked that it held all of the available emergency medications, including intravenous saline.

It was about nine o'clock on that Saturday morning in late August when we set off. The pony was tasked with carrying my bag, two umbrellas, a blanket, a large polythene sheet, a towel, a change of underwear and my shower-proof jacket. I asked Sante to accompany me. I told the men that they would have to pay some money to Sante, to which they readily agreed. I did not want to ride the pony and opted to walk instead. It is OK to ride a little but if one is not accustomed to it, one can hardly walk straight the next day. As a mark of respect to me neither of the men rode and the little beast must have felt greatly relieved.

We crossed Khalanga Bazaar (Jumla's central market square) and proceeded over the narrow wooden footbridge to a village on the other side. A group of half-naked urchins with beautiful smiles and gorgeous bright eyes joined our party. They laughed and danced and made up their own songs about a doctor going to see a patient. They would return home after a little fun and another group from another village would join in due course.

The mountains were at their most beautiful with a myriad of wild flowers and greenery. The sun was shining after continuous rain for three days. This was a very welcome break in the monsoon, which isolated us from the rest of the world for three months every year. During this period, the twenty-seat Twin Otter plane service would be suspended from its once-a-week charter, as flying was too dangerous due to low clouds and the soggy grass runway. Luckily, it would soon end and the plane services would resume by mid-September.

The trail was along the side of the Tila, a deep tributary of the great Karnali River. It was relatively flat considering the great height of the surrounding mountains. We could maintain a good speed. Our destination was a village that had natural thermal springs and hence was called *Tatopani*, hot water. The hot-water springs were said to have medicinal properties, similar to other sulphurous springs elsewhere in the world. Local people enjoyed this natural boon, but it had not been commercially exploited for tourists. After a little break for a quick bite and some rest we continued as fast as we could. We reached the village just after midday.

The patient was lying on his back on a *radi* (coarse woollen rug), which was spread over a layer of hay in one corner of the cowshed. Two of the cows were tethered nearby. One wooden bench, some *mudhas* (hand-made stools crafted from wood, leather and rope), a few *pirkas* (low wooden seats, usually kept in the kitchen and used for seating at meal times) were scattered near the patient and some were occupied.

The women folk were sitting a little further away on a *sukul* (large mat made of hay or the leaves covering cobs of maize). The patient made a feeble attempt to sit up and joined his hands in *namaste* (greeting) but this was too much of an effort. He fell back upon the *radi,* exhausted and obviously in pain.

I needed some privacy for him but there was no door to shut. I therefore asked all the people gathered in the cowshed to move as far away as possible. At first, Sante hesitated to touch the patient in case he defiled him. One stern disapproving look from me while I was touching the patient myself hastily brought him to my assistance. I sat by the patient upon one of those *mudhas* and began my work.

He was a thinly built man. I learnt that he was about sixty years old. He had been relatively well until a few months before when the urinary symptoms had commenced. He had started to leak continuously soon afterwards. This had stopped three days before when he had returned from cremating his father. He was extremely uncomfortable and could not sit up without getting severe pain. He had shivers and felt very ill. I could see his distended abdomen. This history suggested a case of acute on chronic urinary retention with superadded urinary infection. What was the cause? Was he septic as well? These questions were soon answered when I examined him. He was hot as a furnace with a bounding rapid pulse. I looked at his genitals. The penis was buried within a big scrotal swelling, which was a left inguinal hernia, luckily reducible. I turned him onto his side. I put on a surgical glove and dipped my finger into the tub of petroleum jelly. He screamed obscenities when I performed a digital rectal examination. The prostate was enlarged from the size of a walnut to the size of a small pear. It was very hard and irregular, most likely malignant.

I removed my gloves. His wife poured water from an *umkhara* (a kind of water jug made of bronze) so that I could wash my hands. I had my own piece of soap in my bag. I gave the man a shot of Streptopenicillin, a commercial preparation combining streptomycin and procaine penicillin. Penicillin probably would be of no help but streptomycin would surely do the trick. Unfortunately, I did not have pure streptomycin. Penicillin was an unnecessary waste. I then proceeded to try to insert a catheter.

Little did I realise that this simple act would prove to be one of the greatest challenges of my life as a doctor. I defy anyone to catheterise a man who is groaning in agony, lying on the floor in a dimly lit cow-shed, using a soft rubber catheter through a shrunken penis buried in a huge scrotal swelling. I began to sweat. The elusive urethral meatus (opening) would magically vanish at times making me realise that I was pushing the catheter into the soft scrotal mound. The 'no touch technique' (a special technique of catheter insertion without directly touching it) went out of the cowshed. It was now the 'grab somehow and push it in technique'. My two hands were not sufficient. I made Sante hold on to the penis and keep it pulled out as far as possible. At last, I could feel the obstruction at the base of the bladder. But it would not give way. I tried gently to push the catheter only to see its tip peeping out of the glans. It had coiled and doubled back. I started all over again, this time changing the direction of the push a little. I tried to push it a little more firmly into the bladder but it simply coiled back once again. The eye of the catheter tip would appear to mock me in my attempts to push it into the bladder. It defied all my efforts with fresh catheters as well. All I had was a packet of soft rubber catheters, no firm ones. Even his internal sphincter appeared to have gone into spasm, squeezing the membranous urethra. I tried guiding the tip of the catheter with one finger in the rectum but no matter how I tried, I could not enter the bladder neck. My poor patient was begging, 'Please doctor, let the water out.'

It was useless to try any further. I did not have a metal catheter and I did not know how to insert a supra pubic one. The patient was clearly in agony. What was I to do?

I explained to him that the soft rubber catheter was not able to enter the bladder. His wife got very upset thinking that her husband would be the next to die.

I decided to puncture the bladder with a hypodermic needle and drain the urine with the help of a syringe. That would give me some time and the patient would get some relief. I selected the largest syringe I had, a ten millilitre glass and metal antique, which had been sterilised the previous day. Choosing a point just above the symphysis pubis, I boldly inserted the needle into the abdomen.

The piston flew off the top of the syringe and landed on a heap of cow dung, just as the urine spurted like a jet fountain, narrowly missing Sante and myself. I never expected to see this! The villagers clapped; my patient's wife smiled. I do not know which was more difficult for me, to keep a straight face or to hold the syringe in place. The spectacle did not last long and the fountain soon died down. The patient stopped groaning. Keeping the needle in place, I disconnected the barrel and attached it to another syringe, this time five millilitres in size. It probably took me a couple of hours to drain as much urine as possible. His abdomen became flat and the patient was able to fall asleep intermittently. The villagers drifted away now that the excitement was over.

I explained that the patient would need an injection of Streptopenicillin daily for the next four days. I also explained that he would very likely go into retention again and hence he should come to the hospital. I had no idea how I was going to catheterise him even if he did but I would think of something, I said to myself. There were immediate protestations in response to this advice. How can a *kiria-putri* (the person observing *kiria*) walk away from the chosen spot and be hospitalised? It would be unthinkable and the priest would not allow it. The spirit of the ancestors would surely take offence at such an act of sacrilege. I did not get into any debate. I said brusquely that I had only been successful temporarily and it was up to them to decide. I left with Sante.

The consultation had been very long. I did not have time to have a dip in the hot spring. What a disappointment that was. Travelling at night in that part of the world was always dangerous. Huge Tibetan mastiffs would be released from their metal chains after the evening meal to guard the homes in the villages. These dogs would bite you before the villagers asked for introductions. We hurried back home.

As expected, my advice was not accepted. Nobody brought the patient the next day. The day after, however, a group of villagers arrived at the hospital. They had brought the patient at the insistence of his wife. She had dared to defy the family priest and the ancient customs. But there was more to the story.

The patient had begun to feel a little better the day after my heroic intervention, yet he had still not been able to pass urine. His abdomen had begun to swell up again on the second night. By the third morning he was in agony once more. The nausea and shivers had also returned.

The village *jhankri* (similar to a witch doctor) had been summoned. He went to the bank of the River Tila and brought a long narrow straight reed. He managed to scrape out the insides of this reed and had sharpened one end to a point. This end he had lubricated with *gheu* (clarified butter) and had introduced it gently into the penis. He had pushed it all the way through, assuring the man that this would 'let the water out'. But this act had not succeeded in draining urine, only blood. The reed had been removed but the bleeding would not stop. The patient was getting worse. His wife had then taken charge and decided to bring her husband to the hospital against all conventions.

This patient presented quite a number of logistical problems. He needed a separate secluded area near a stream so that he could continue with his mourning rituals. The hospital porters cleared a shed which had been used to store all kinds of junk. This was cleaned and a hospital bed was installed so that the patient could be made comfortable.

Next was the question of draining urine. The urethral route was now impossible. I had to drain it with hypodermic needles and a small syringe twice a day. My only hope was to wait for the trauma to heal and for the false passage to close over the next few days. Intramuscular antibiotics controlled the infection. The patient began to feel much better. The urethral bleeding had stopped for a few days when day eleven since the cremation arrived and pressure was put on me to allow him to return home for the thirteenth-day celebrations.

I had no idea as to how I was going to catheterise him. I wrestled with the dilemma that evening and eventually fell into a deep sleep whilst trying to think of a solution. I woke up refreshed and calm the next morning. It was day twelve.

There was an old, broken umbrella. In silence I ripped it apart and managed to salvage two long, metal spokes. There were worried glances in my direction. I called our maid, Maya, and asked her to boil those two spokes in the largest cooking vessel that we had. Nobody dared to ask me a question, yet I was sure that all would have doubted my sanity.

I went to the hospital and began to get the catheterisation kit ready. Maya fetched the huge saucepan with the boiled spokes in it. I inserted one into the largest catheter and bent the distal end into a gentle curve. It was now firm and malleable without being hard. My idea appeared to be workable.

Sante held the penis as an expert this time. After a liberal splashing of petroleum jelly and a silent prayer, I inserted the catheter into the urethra and gently guided it through towards the base of the bladder. With the other finger in the rectum, I tried to feel the catheter tip and adjusted the direction appropriately. With some gentle manipulation I was able to negotiate the membranous urethra. A little push and, miraculously, it gave. A drop of urine appeared. I pushed it further and removed the spoke of the umbrella. Urine was draining nice and clear.

I secured the catheter as well as I could and put the fear of God into the patient, lest he carelessly pull it out. All I had was a cheap rubber catheter for single use. I did not have the expensive silicone-coated Foley's catheter that could be left in the bladder for several weeks. I advised him to go to Nepalgunj as soon as the plane services resumed. I gave him a supply of Nitrofurantoin to take prophylactically.

Sitting down to a late breakfast in the front garden, I watched the poor man walk home to do his duty to his departed parent. Sante came holding the reed tubing. 'What shall I do with this?' he asked.

CHAPTER 7

Toothache

Jumla Hospital, officially named 'Karnali Zonal Hospital', was little better than a ramshackle collection of three stone and slate buildings, without electricity, running water or sanitation, or equipment, or medication.

We used to work for about three hours every morning. We could comfortably see a dozen or so patients during this time. There was little else to do thereafter. From the late mornings until five in the afternoon when I would meet other officers at the *tundikhel* (village green) for our daily game of football, one had to be creative to keep occupied. Life was tranquil, often painfully so. My wife, Leela, was the other doctor. We had a four-year-old son, Nandan. We would play chess and make up our own games.

From the front garden of our house, we could see the sharp bend in the trail to the south leading to Khalanga Bazaar, the main village square. This was also marked by a saffron flag fluttering over the shrine of a monk. Coming away from the village this trail continued northward after passing the hospital gate, which was about thirty yards in front of our house. This was the main route towards the Danfe pass, situated at seventeen thousand feet, leading to Rara Lake in Mugu and then further north to Simkot in Humla. This section was about half a mile in length. One could see all sorts walking on this wide mountain trail until they reached the hospital gate, at which point they would be close enough to be identified. It had become a kind of guessing game for Nandan and me. We would identify these walking objects as patients, soldiers, trekkers, yaks or cows when they were just a distant blur. The person who had correctly guessed first would win. But on the day in question the distant multicoloured blur did not match any of our usual patterns. Nandan said that it was a giant from his book 'Jack and the Beanstalk'. To me it looked rather like a moving tent surrounded by people. It was very curious. We continued to watch until the blur arrived at the hospital gate twenty minutes later.

It was a cot (a wooden bedstead) lifted high and carried on the shoulders of several men. There was a woman sitting on the cot accompanied by another form which was lying curled up and covered with a bright coloured blanket. There were four other men in the group. They headed towards the out-patient block. Nandan and I reached there as the cot was being placed on the ground. 'Daddy, patient!' said Nandan, obviously disappointed that our game could no longer be continued. He sauntered back towards the house.

The newcomers had left their village in Sinja the previous day to carry this patient to the hospital. They had spent the night in Tatopani and resumed their trek at dawn.

The patient, Lachmi, was a fifteen-year-old girl. She was the only child of rich parents. She had complained of a bad tooth ache at first. A long sharp thorn had been used to pierce the point of pain without any improvement. She had subsequently developed a temperature which had not responded to herbal treatment. She was getting worse. She had been unable to eat anything and could not open her mouth.

The villagers had decided to bring her to Jumla, normally a three-day walk from their village. She had been unable to drink fluids and had become delirious on the way. The previous night she had begun to develop convulsions and could no longer be carried on a *doko* (large basket) on the back of a *bharia* (porter). Hence they had transferred her to a cot. Her mother sat with her and had been applying a cold compress throughout. Her father had come as well. Lachmi had had no convulsions for about an hour but was hardly conscious.

The history indicated a severe septic condition. When I examined her she looked toxic, with the left side of her face greatly swollen. She was flushed with fever, dehydrated and very hot to touch, with a quick thin pulse and rapid but not irregular breathing, and was obviously post ictal (in a state of drowsiness after a seizure). There was a black speck just under her lower jaw on the left side but it was mostly obscured by swelling. She had wet herself earlier, probably during the convulsions, so I knew that part of her system was working OK. Her neck was not stiff and there were no blotches on her skin suggestive of meningitis.

After this cursory examination, I decided first to stabilise her condition. I began to hunt for appropriate medications in our hospital stores. The minimal yearly supply of medicines had run out within a few months. I found that we had stacks of Plaster of Paris and gauze bandages and a lot of assorted suture materials. We also had a large supply of contraceptive pills, vitamin A and D capsules and a few menstrual regulating kits. There were several intra-uterine contraceptive device (IUD) insertion packs. We used to get some medical supplies occasionally from the foreign trekkers returning from Rara. Our recent acquisition had been a large box of intravenous fluids and several vials of intravenous Reverin, a powerful antibiotic with a broad spectrum of activity. These would prove very useful.

A saline drip was rapidly set up. I gave the patient a shot of paraldehyde because that was the only anti-seizure drug I had in the hospital. I had no penicillin, nor metronidazole. The plane from Kathmandu was not due for another six days. I gave a massive starting dose of Reverin and maintained a steady administration of this antibiotic with the intravenous drip. I wrote a prescription for Streptopen, a penicillin and streptomycin combination which was quite popular in those days. The local grocery shop sometimes kept these drugs to sell at exorbitant prices. Lachmi's father went to *Khalanga Bazaar* and returned with the supply for me to administer.

Now it was a question of waiting. By the evening, Lachmi was a little better. Her pulse was stronger and steady. Her systolic blood pressure had returned to a respectable level. Her breathing was still rapid but not so laboured. She had had no further convulsions. Her bladder was full and I hoped that she would pass urine normally.

However, her temperature remained over 104 degrees Fahrenheit. I had examined her in detail earlier in the day. The tense swelling between her lower jaw and neck was probably her left mandibular lymph node grossly enlarged. The small black speck over her lower cheek was actually the root of her lower left first molar which had penetrated through the skin! She could not open her mouth for me to examine inside it. I could find no other source of infection.

Her parents were a little comforted. Although they were rich, they were not rich enough to charter a plane to take their daughter to Kathmandu. They were depending upon me to cure her. I returned from my football game that evening and saw her again. She appeared stable. I hoped that once the antibiotics got working, she would be out of septic shock and that the infection would become localised within the next day. Then it would be a simple matter of tooth extraction. Unfortunately she had not passed urine. She needed to be catheterised after the infusion of four litres of intravenous fluids.

She remained the same the next day. Her temperature did not drop and the swelling in her face did not diminish. I began secretly to panic. The steady antibiotic and intravenous fluid infusion was continued. By midnight, her blood pressure had begun to drop a little. She developed a minor seizure about six in the morning. I had no alternative. I had to remove the offending tooth if she was to have a chance of survival.

I looked at our instrument cabinet. We had a few sets of equipment to introduce Lippes loop (an intrauterine contraceptive device) into the womb. There was one needle holder, one rather ancient artery forceps, and suture materials. That was all I had. I had no other surgical instruments of any description. How was I to operate?

With my spirits rapidly sinking, I goaded myself to think, improvise and show some initiative. 'How can you allow a young girl to die? What kind of a doctor are you?' I chided myself.

How was I to open her mouth and keep it open? I had no oral speculum. I needed a long scalpel to cut through the bone; a few artery forceps to stop the bleeding; and a tooth extractor to pull the tooth out. I had none of these things. Absentmindedly, I opened one of the IUD packs. And *Lord Pashupatinath* gave me inspiration.

I went to the parents and explained that unless I operated on Lachmi and took the offending tooth out, blood poisoning would kill her. Even the operation might not prevent death, but at least we would have tried to save her as far as possible. I also explained that I did not have sufficient equipment but I would try somehow. The alternative was unthinkable. The mother started to cry loudly, clutching the semi-conscious girl. Her husband took her out of the room and returned a little later. With joined hands, he said that he had every faith in me and that I should go ahead with the operation. This was a heavy burden of responsibility upon my young shoulders. He eased it somewhat by adding, 'If the Gods want Lachmi in heaven, we will not be able to hold her here.' It was seven AM.

I instructed Mrs Shanta Shrestha, the Assistant Nurse Midwife (ANM) to boil the instruments for IUD insertion along with the needle holder, the artery forceps, and a few shaving blades from my safety razor. I asked her to get lots of gauze and cotton swabs as well. There was an old steel operating table in one of the clean rooms in the hospital. I asked her to set it up for the operation in an hour. She was bewildered but managed to keep quiet.

I had a conference with Leela and she too agreed that we had no other choice. Open ether anaesthetic could precipitate convulsions. We would prevent this by giving paraldehyde first. Is this done? Is it safe? We had no idea. It appeared logical and we were prepared to take this risk. The alternative was an almost certain death. We took Lachmi to the operating room. One more shot of paraldehyde and some drops of open ether later, and she was flat out. Leela took over the anaesthetic aspect.

I asked for Cusco's vaginal speculum and gently inserted it into Lachmi's mouth. Shanta was desperately trying to stop herself from laughing. I was completely serious but shaking in my boots with nerves. I began to rotate the screw of the speculum to open the blades as much as possible. The blades held and gave me adequate access into Lachmi's mouth. Next, I needed the artery forceps holding gauze pieces soaked in dilute antiseptic and saline to swab the insides of her mouth. My pen torch came in useful and one of the porters was tasked with focusing the beam of light. Most of the crown had disappeared from the offending first molar. I could not have pulled the tooth out with an extractor even if I had had one. I needed to cut the jaw to dig the root out. I swore silently. Next, I broke one shaving blade into two, clamping one of the pieces in the artery forceps. I had to tie the blade sideways to hold it firmly. This became my scalpel with a long handle. It was the volsellum (narrow curved tongs used to grasp and hold the mouth of the cervix) which was now used to swab the blood. I started gently to cut along the direction of the root of the rotten molar. The tip of the uterine sound (a narrow round metal rod, bent at an angle, to examine the interior of the womb) helped to prize out the molar root. Eventually, I was able to grab the root between the teeth of the volsellum. I pulled and the root came out of its socket. Halleluiah! I lifted it out of Lachmi's mouth and put it on a kidney tray. Luckily, the blood vessels in the jaw had escaped being cut. The bleeding was not significant but a lot of pus began to ooze out. The swelling below her jaw began to shrink quite visibly. It must have been a large tooth abscess. I drained it as much as I could. Shanta's swabs in generous supply came in handy. This must have been the only oral surgery of its kind ever to have been performed.

I cleaned the rotten tooth and gave it to Lachmi's mother as a souvenir. I asked them to pray as there was nothing more we could do. Lachmi was unconscious until lunch time when I went to my quarters. I saw her again before going for my football game, although I debated whether I should be going at all that evening. Lachmi's mother pointed at me and said to her daughter, 'He is the doctor, do *namaste* to him.' I saw two large tired eyes which were no longer bloodshot, in a face which was still swollen but no longer flushed with fever. Her pulse had slowed down and was strong. She was breathing normally. She would survive! I had to suppress my urge to shout with joy and remember that I was the dignified doctor who could not express these emotions. How can doctors remain objective and impersonal? I wanted to cry.

I do not remember much of that evening except that I scored a goal from my usual position of full back. The 'tooth mark' on Lachmi's lower cheek would remain as a scar. I teased her that it would be a beauty spot. She returned home with her parents after a week. I smile to myself sometimes when I remember how the surgery was performed. What would Lachmi say if she knew?

CHAPTER 8

A Tryst With Treponema

It was 1974 in Jumla, Western Nepal, during my time as a Medical Officer. A handsome man in his late twenties sat, restless and uncomfortable, in front of my desk. There was clearly something on his mind. He had returned from the Indian city of Lucknow the previous week and chattered nervously about his journey in a mixture of English, Nepali and Hindi. Still unaware of the medical complaint, although with suspicions in place, I listened patiently to his stories.

It was a bright and beautiful morning. I had finished seeing my patients and was taking a moment to enjoy a cup of tea when the man had arrived. At first I was unsure as to whether he had come as a patient or to make a social call. He was a government officer working in the area and employed by the Indian Mission to supervise a number of small rural projects along the Nepal-Tibet border, aided by the Indian government. I knew that he was actually a spy. I asked for a second cup of tea, just in case it was a social visit after all.

Throughout the garbled narrative I looked at him intently. 'Would you like me to have a look at you?' I interrupted, by now certain of my suspicions.

The relief and surprise were both visible in his face. He turned crimson and asked, 'How did you know?' I had hit the bull's-eye. My hunch was right.

'That is my trade secret,' I said, rising to close the door and shutters.

It was a classic syphilitic chancre, no question about that. Also present were obviously painless bilateral 'bubos' in his groin. My patient's handsome features contorted with his self-inflicted shame and humiliation. He rapidly pulled on his pants. A souvenir from Lucknow, I thought.

I always remembered my teacher Professor Sambashivan's warning that 'respectability is no bar to the penetrating ability of *Treponema pallidum*.' (*Treponema pallidum* is the bacterium that causes syphilis.) The hospital had no laboratory or any investigative facilities. One depended entirely on one's clinical skills to make a diagnosis. The place was the poorest one could imagine.

'Tell me, is your wife with you?' I asked.

'No, I left her with her parents in Bareily last month when I went to Lucknow. I had never been to a *mujra* before, you see. It was my first time; my friends forced me. I got carried away. Please, help me,' he implored.

Lucknow was once notorious for its prostitutes. Although prostitution had been officially banned in India, the profession thrived under a different guise. Prostitutes would call themselves courtesans and trade through dance halls as it was legal to pursue dancing and singing as a profession. They would sing and dance in cheap imitation of the accomplished Mogul courtesans, accompanied by pimps posing as musicians. The price for sex following the musical evening, called a *mujra*, would be negotiated and the business conducted in secrecy from the patrolling police outside, who often overlooked such dealings in return for a quick freebie.

My patient informed me he had had no sexual intercourse with his wife since returning home; he further denied any other contact. That was something to be thankful for, I thought with relief. I confirmed the diagnosis of syphilis, and assured my patient that it was curable. The treatment was a painful course of twelve long-acting penicillin injections given deep intramuscularly into the gluteal muscles of the buttocks. For some, this treatment served as a firm deterrent from future promiscuity; others were not so dispirited.

I made arrangements for his treatment. He would come to see me after my morning work and pretend it to be a social visit. I would give him the daily injection. We would have a cup of tea, smoke his expensive 555 cigarettes, then he would limp away.

Later that week, I was visited by a female patient. Normally most women would go to Leela, particularly if they had any gynaecological complaints. This lady, however, had said she wanted to see me and not Leela.

She was a beautiful woman in her thirties. She had had no children and had a provocative figure. I recognised her as Menaka, the wife of the Land Distribution Officer. She was regularly alone for days whilst her husband travelled across the four districts in Karnali zone.

She sat on a chair in front of my desk and began to twist the corner of her sari. Her hesitation and discomfiture were clear. I asked if she would prefer to see Leela.

'No. I want you to see me, if you don't mind?' she asked. I understood that it was a confidential consultation and she could not trust even a female doctor with her secrets.

'As you wish', I said, getting up to find Sita, the chaperone.

'No!' she screamed in terror.

I came back, calmed her down and encouraged her to speak.

Wincing with shame, she showed me her groin. I understood, finally.

She was remarkably candid in allowing me to examine her. Like the spy, she also had a classic syphilitic chancre, in her case over her left labia, together with painless bubos on both sides. It looked almost identical to the one I had recently seen.

'How is your husband?' I asked.

She shrugged. 'Don't know. Must be somewhere looking for presents for me,' she murmured.

Her meaning was unmistakable. She evidently blamed him for her venereal infection. I said that he too would need treatment and that she should bring him to me upon his return. She made a face, cursed him, and said that widowhood appeared to be very desirable.

To maintain her confidentiality I advised that she come to me for treatment first thing in the mornings, before the hospital opened its Outpatient Clinic. She could therefore avoid meeting Sita or Leela.

It was unusual for Menaka to miss an appointment. The morning she did not attend coincided with the final day of treatment for my male patient, the spy. He came as usual. He opened a fresh packet of cigarettes and we had a cup of tea together. I gave him his injection. He promised to bring us a present from Bareily the following week when he would be going there to fetch his wife. He left, deliberately leaving the new packet of 555s. I smiled.

'*Ammain, hyan kina?*' ('Hey, why are you here?') I heard a female voice exclaim outside. Hushed whispers ensued, shortly followed by a knock on my door. Menaka stood before me with a pot of chicken curry. It was my turn to be surprised. Her husband had arrived unexpectedly the previous evening, evidently explaining her non-attendance at the hospital that morning. She had made the curry, her husband's favourite, after he had arrived. She had then thought of this pretext.

'I said to him that your little son liked chicken. I asked him whether I could send some of the left-overs to the hospital,' she explained. He had agreed quietly, appearing distracted. He knew that she liked giving sweets and chocolates to little children as they had no children of their own.

My patient confirmed that nothing physical had happened the night before. She said that he was too tired and fell asleep immediately. I gave her her injection. Seven more to go. She assured me that she would think of some excuse and come tomorrow. The chicken dish was very tasty, yet Leela was not pleased to receive the gift. Her disinclination to take a second helping told me what she thought of the whole affair. Later, I heard her telling Maya, our maid, that there was no need to save any for the evening meal. She could eat as much as she liked and give the rest away.

Late that afternoon, half reclined in post-prandial drowsiness, I abruptly sat bolt upright. All the connections became apparent in that instant. The convenience of the situation was abundantly clear. Why would a wife welcome home an unfaithful husband and cook a precious chicken in his honour, when she had told me earlier that she would probably kill him on his return for infecting her with syphilis? The chancre and the clinical presentation were identical. The patients lived in adjoining houses. The sudden unguarded exclamations and whispers outside my consulting room earlier now made sense. Well, both are being treated, I thought. I chuckled at the latest revelation of the local soap opera. Did she know that the spy could have given her the infection? Was it the fear of her own guilt that had prevented her from taking her husband to task?

'*Namaste,* Doctor *saheb.* How was the chicken?' enquired a booming voice from behind. I turned to find Bishu, the Land Distribution Officer, smiling at me.

I thanked him for the delicious gift and returned his *namaste.* I pointed to a chair and offered a 555, courtesy of his wife's lover. I smiled inwardly. Life can always be made interesting, even in a desolate place like Jumla.

'How was your trip?' I asked to start a conversation. He explained that the trip had been particularly difficult. He had cut it short and returned early. Many farmers had mortgaged their land to money lenders who possessed the deeds which he could not access. He continued to describe the difficulties in doing his work whilst I patiently waited for him to come to the real reason for his visit. The initial mention of the chicken probably indicated that I had to return the favour in some way.

'There is a private matter,' he said at last, scratching his temple. I looked around. There was no-one nearby. He pretended to see a midge on his forearm and swatted it with his hand. He stood up and took a deep drag of the cigarette. He sat down again and blurted out, 'The witch has killed me.' I was not surprised. I had already figured that out. But it was necessary to get more information.

'Which woman and what happened?' I asked, foolishly believing that I already knew the answer.

'Kanchi Kathini. She has given me the clap.' The seething anger and frustration were clearly audible, in spite of his weak whisper. This was totally unexpected. I could not have been more wrong in my assumptions. I took him to the privacy of my consulting room.

First, I examined him. He had the identical chancre and bubos. Clap refers to gonorrhoea, not syphilis, but its translation in Nepali '*viringi*' is the same for both. I told him of the diagnosis and assured him that it was a curable disease. Kanchi Kathini was a bit of puzzle, however.

I knew of Kanchi Kathini of Mugu. She had come herself to the hospital several months earlier for a minor complaint. She had flashed me a smile of thank you and had offered the shelter of her house if I was ever in the vicinity. I was new in the area and had thought nothing of this polite conversation. At that time there were no inns or hotels in the mountains of western Nepal. One sought overnight accommodation in any house that happened to be close by. Mugu is still one of the most deprived areas in the country, although it has the most beautiful lake in the world, the Rara Taal. I had thanked her and she had gone away.

Later on, I had been informed by our field officer for the control of smallpox that Kanchi Kathini bestowed special favours upon rich tourists and important government officers. I had come to know subsequently of a few other officers who had received her special favours. They had not acknowledged my concerns about contracting venereal disease from her. They had assured me that she used always to make them wear condoms because her husband had been away for a while. She would not want to get pregnant while he was away and face the consequences upon his return. So it was unlikely that she had infected our friend here.

There was no point in telling my latest patient that it was not Kanchi Kathini but his own wife who had been the source of his infection. Silence would ensure that he would never again go near the former. It was, however, necessary to tell Menaka that the source of her infection was her lover and not her husband. This way she would never again go near the spy. She had to be told that it was she who had infected her husband.

I arranged for Bishu to come daily for injections. His wife would not suspect the arrangements, I assured him. It was not a lie. Suspicion was not even a factor when she knew for sure. I cautioned against intercourse for a full two weeks. I asked him to send his wife to the hospital because he could not be sure when the infection had been acquired.

It was very welcome to Menaka that her husband had asked her to see us at the hospital. He had told her that she needed to be examined to find out why she had had no children. She came regularly for the next seven days, now without excuses. This allowed her to complete her course of injections under the pretext of treatment for infertility. Leela did examine her subsequently to find a large, bulky retroverted uterus which required treatment in Kathmandu.

Menaka broke down and cried bitterly when I enquired of the spy. She accepted that they had flirted just to spite her husband, whom she had known to be unfaithful for a long time. She had desperately wanted children but he was not interested. She had succumbed to temptation by the spy on one occasion, only to receive severe punishment from the Gods, she believed.

The spy returned to see me a month later, accompanied by his pregnant wife. She must have conceived when he was infectious. This complicated matters further. I confronted him, cautioning that he had put his own and others' lives and marriages in danger. He denied everything at first and acted greatly offended. It was after pointing out that the unborn child was probably infected and would most likely be stillborn that he came clean. He owned up to all his exploits. He had been a regular customer of many brothels, apparently an occupational hazard of his job. I should not have been, but remember feeling very angry at that flippant remark.

Acting outside my remit as a doctor I warned the spy to stop visiting brothels and other women, or else I would put a word in the ear of the Zonal Commissioner who was my friend. He would lose both his job and his wife. Pulling both his ears in a most contrite manner, he swore upon his unborn child never to visit a brothel again and to remain faithful thereafter.

He agreed to bring his wife to Leela for a check-up. She was about sixteen weeks pregnant. An innocent young village girl, she had not learnt to speak Nepali and did not know any English. Her husband was employed to interpret, opportunely inventing reasons for the twelve painful injections in her buttock. None of the other women in the village had told her that one needed to have so many injections during pregnancy. I did not wish to shatter the life of an innocent young mother-to-be by telling her the real reason for the treatment. Her husband had accepted his fault and promised to behave responsibly. There is nothing to be gained by exposing the truth, I thought.

Just before we left Jumla, the spy brought us some sweets from Bareily where his wife had delivered a big healthy boy. I asked him whether the boy had a depressed nose, which is a sign of congenital syphilis. He was puzzled. I remember being relieved when he showed me the photograph of his newborn son. It is thought that most syphilitic congenital malformations occur in the first three months of pregnancy.

Much later, I happened to meet Bishu and Menaka and their two children in Kathmandu. They were both most grateful for what I had done.

I do not know if Kanchi Kathini ever found out why all of the touring government officers had ceased to seek shelter in her house, if indeed they had done so. She was the only one who suffered in the long term; her source of fun, and income, had dried up!

CHAPTER 9

Mismanagement

'*Jadau, Saheb,*' ('Greetings, Sir') said the shadow which suddenly hovered over me. It was a bright morning after the relentless week-long downpour of rain heralding the monsoon. I was sitting on a makeshift chair on the front porch of my living quarters, enjoying the soft caress of the sun's rays on my face. Our living quarters served as the office and hospital store as well. The building had a mud roof, parts of which would continue to drip inside long after the rain had ceased. We had slept the previous night by strategically placing three umbrellas over the bed.

I was waiting for some breakfast before starting the morning clinic. Perhaps I had dozed off a little. I squinted my eyes, trying to open them. I had to turn sideways to take a good look at the cause of this sudden intrusion.

A tall skeleton of a man was bending over me with clasped hands. He had a long staff between them, the upper end of which was resting over one shoulder. Suspended from it was a little bundle. His clothes were torn and filthy. He was barefoot. His cap, once made of bright colourful *dhaka* (a hand woven cloth with delicate patterns), was now a faded crumpled rag over his head. A few days of dark stubble, interspersed with grey, covered his chin. Startled, I stood up, returned his salutation and motioned to a *mudha* (a hand-made stool of rough leather and reeds) for him to sit. He chose to sit on the damp floor instead. Two other people with a *doko* (a large basket made of bamboo) were sitting outside the garden fence, several feet away.

It was in 1973 in Jumla, where Leela and I had been sent by the health ministry as medical officers. Jumla was the regional head quarters of Karnali, a rugged area of great natural beauty. It stood 2500 meters above sea level, in the far western region of Nepal, bordering Tibet. It is still one of the most deprived areas and the people are very poor. The hospital was called Karnali Zonal Hospital, a rather grandiose name for an institution which was hardly a hospital.

The in-patient building had a slate roof without any insulation. It had mud floors and tiny windows. There were ten wooden cots with two blankets on each – one to spread and the other to cover oneself. Besides us two doctors there were two auxiliary nurse midwives, ten porters and one *mukhia* (a very junior clerk). Our work force was tasked with providing health care for nearly fifty thousand people over an area of about five thousand square miles. The place was accessible in fair weather by a small plane from Kathmandu; otherwise, one had to trek northwards from Nepalgunj for thirteen days to reach this remote place.

The out-patient building had just been given a mud roof with polythene sheeting underneath. The villagers had donated their labour for the benefit of the hospital. This building had two rooms – one for treatment, the other for consulting. The nearby stream provided cold water for washing. Two of the porters were at that moment busy fetching buckets of the water needed to prepare for surgery. We had to boil instruments, syringes and needles on a kerosene stove.

The medical supplies arrived from Nepalgunj in October and would last until December. For the rest of the year, we could not dispense any medications. Patients bought medications from Nepalgunj or Kathmandu privately. The hospital was by the side of the main route for trekking to Rara Lake. We had learnt to be very hospitable to foreign tourists so that they would leave their unused medical supplies with us, which we would then use sparingly for the local patients.

'*Kina aunubho?*' ('What can I do for you?') I asked the stranger. Slowly he untied his bundle and retrieved a small *thaili* (cloth purse).

He placed this purse on my feet and, clutching my ankles, said very reverentially, '*Malai jogaideu.*' ('Please save me.') I was startled and rather bewildered. I listened to what he had to say.

He was a poor village cobbler from Simkot in Humla, a nine-day trek from where we were. He had been ill for several months and had lost a lot of weight. His wife had since run away with another man, a travelling salesman who had come to the village. He had no children and no-one to look after him. He had recently started to cough up blood. The local indigenous healers had tried in vain to help by cutting a rooster and performing various *pooja* (religious rituals to ward off evil spirits). Someone had then advised him to go to the hospital in Jumla. He had sold his hut and a small piece of land for eight hundred rupees, about forty pounds sterling in those days – his entire personal wealth. Around one hundred rupees had already been spent paying for travelling expenses and the wages of the two porters who had carried him in the *doko*. He had been too breathless and weak to walk. He was giving *me* all the remaining money so that I would cure him. He continued to grip my ankles tightly, his sunken eyes beseeching me for the assurance that he would be cured.

I was alarmed. I looked at him again closely. The expression on his face appeared to say that I was his saviour and that only I could rescue him from death. His eyes, full of entreaty and expectation, pierced my soul. His name was Sarkidai. He was about forty years old but looked much older. The swelling and scars on his neck, no doubt due to cold abscesses in childhood, his emaciated body, pale skin, soft voice, and breathlessness on minimal exertion all told me that this man probably had advanced tuberculosis. It was very common in that part of the country and he was likely to die soon. I felt despondent but did my best to maintain a neutral face. I stood up and took a few steps backwards. He was thus forced to free my ankles. How was I going to help this man?

Tuberculosis needs to be treated with a combination of several drugs such as rifampicin, ethambutol, streptomycin and isoniazid. Treatment with a single drug leads to the development of resistant strains of bacteria which can make the disease fatal in due course. I had not been supplied with these powerful medications but a trekking group of American tourists had left some supplies on their way back to

Kathmandu and I had discovered to my surprise a few boxes of isoniazid tablets among other things. I had neither a microscope nor any staining materials to examine sputum for *Mycobacterium tuberculosis*, the organism that causes the illness.

'I must think of some way,' I told myself. I wondered how physicians treated TB before the advent of antibiotics. I decided to admit Sarkidai to the empty hospital. I called the *mukhia* and asked him to put the bag of money in the office safe.

There were no other patients in the in-patient block. A physical examination confirmed my suspicion of tuberculosis – the amphoric breathing over the right apex with signs of bilateral pleural effusion and blood-stained dirty sputum were corroborating evidence. I allowed him the use of half of all the blankets.

The *mukhia* was authorised to spend twenty-five rupees of the hospital budget daily on buying food for Sarkidai. He was to eat three big meals each day, with ghee, rice and one whole chicken. He was encouraged to eat unlimited quantities of apples, which were available in abundance. Potatoes, either boiled or roasted in a coal fire, and honey with *roti* (unleavened bread) were to be made available to eat as snacks in between. One of the porters was named as the designated carer to cook, clean and look after the patient. Other porters took turns giving him exercise. They used to make him walk very slowly within the compound of the hospital.

In addition to clean air, extra nourishment and exercise, I decided to treat him with whatever medications I had at my disposal. I prescribed one and a half times the recommended dose of isoniazid, even though I knew that it would probably not stop him from developing drug resistance. USAID had sent some supplies of multivitamin tablets along with the usual condoms, contraceptive pills and menstrual regulation kits. He was given one of these three times a day. That should prevent the peripheral neuropathy that is associated with isoniazid treatment, I said to myself. My aim was to keep him alive somehow for three months until the monsoon was over.

I planned to send him to Kathmandu on a plane once the air service had resumed. I knew that the proper doctors in Kathmandu would mock my mono-therapy for tuberculosis, especially when they found that the bacilli had become drug resistant. I would be blamed for mismanaging the case as well as the hospital budget. However, I felt that I had no choice.

It was gratifying to see some early signs of improvement in Sarkidai. He began to look better and could walk by himself within a fortnight. He started to smile. He would stand and do *namaste* to me from wherever he was sheltering from the rain or sunning himself, depending upon the weather. Three months passed. I wrote a brief letter of referral and sent him to the TB Hospital in Kalimati, Kathmandu. I did not hear anything about him for nearly a year.

The second monsoon had come and gone a long time before. The plane service from Kathmandu had resumed and people were beginning to prepare for *dasain*, the great annual festival of celebrations and feasting for the Nepalese people. We had had a string of visitors for several weeks. Good food and camaraderie had become possible once again. I was enjoying the morning sunshine outside our living quarters and going through my official correspondence. I had received a strong letter a few days earlier from the internal auditors of the health department demanding an explanation of my unauthorised extra spending. They were querying the expenses that had been incurred feeding Sarkidai. I had used whatever funds had been available at the time but this was obviously unacceptable to the auditors. I wondered what might have happened to Sarkidai. I began to draft an explanatory letter.

'*Jadau, Saheb,*' said a strong voice from behind me. It was a tall man, wearing decent clothes, shoes and a new cap. He had a canvas bag in one hand. He had come to see me before going on to Simkot. It was Sarkidai. He had been treated for nearly a year in Kathmandu and pronounced cured. He was a picture of health and I was delighted to see him.

He said that he had raised his travel expenses by labouring in Kathmandu and Nepalgunj. Then he had walked all the way from Nepalgunj. He wanted to get back to his old life in Simkot, although he had no house, no money and no wife waiting for him there. As for any kind of future, he thought he had none.

'You saved me from *thaksis* (phthisis, or tuberculosis). Will *Budho*

(Lord Buddha) give me back my living?' he despaired. Before going on his way he wanted personally to thank Bale, the porter, who used to cook his meals. I sent for Bale, went into the office, spoke with the *mukhia* and returned to my chair. The *mukhia* came out a few moments later and gave me something from the office safe. Soon after, I wished Sarkidai a safe journey and put something into his hand as a customary gesture of farewell. As expected, he did not take much notice.

He did *namaste* to me again and was about to leave when he looked at his hands. His eyes sparkled in recognition. He clutched at the old *thaili*. He could feel that all of his remaining wealth was intact there. Emotion overflowing uncontrollably from his eyes, he spoke volumes without uttering a word. He could not help staring at me. Then his eyes wandered far away to the north and a glaze came over them. He walked away to the future which moments before he had not believed that he had. The *mukhia*, Bale and I looked on silently until he disappeared over the mountain.

I returned to my paperwork. I still had to complete the letter explaining the budgetary mismanagement.

CHAPTER 10

The Spirit Of The Mountain Stream

It was Saturday morning, clear, bright and frozen at around minus five degrees Celsius. The weekend in Nepal is just one day, Saturday. Normal work begins again on Sunday. I was late in getting up that morning. It was after eight-thirty when I was listening to the English news on the radio that I was informed of the arrival of august visitors.

Our maid Maya might have been impressed by the sight of the Governor, with his two armed bodyguards, accompanied by two Honourable Members of the *Rastria Panchayat* (House of Parliament), coming to the humble living quarters of a district medical officer on a Saturday. The truth of the matter was that doctors working in the districts were continually subjected to tremendous pressure to conform to the autocratic *Panchayat* rule of the late King Birendra. His agents, among whom were included the members of the *Rastria Panchayat,* the Governor and the security officers, got up to all sorts of criminal activities just as they pleased as long as they could show themselves to be in the clear. Medical certificates were vitally important for criminal prosecution, and doctors were therefore extremely valuable. Most doctors would find ways and means of protecting themselves whilst maintaining professional ethics. But tight-rope walking like this was always difficult and extremely risky. It was perhaps ironical that the medical profession was still held in high esteem by the ordinary people.

I did not dare to keep the dignitaries waiting and so came out to greet them, dressed in a thick woollen robe and apologising for my morning laziness. Tea was ordered and served in glass tumblers, sweet and hot. After the usual pleasantries, the Governor informed me that his companions had a tricky problem to discuss. Nandan entered the parlour and ran straight to 'Governor Uncle'. They went out into the front garden to play, joined by Londup, the dog. The two Honourable Members had my undivided attention.

The member from Kholapari district, Honourable Giri, spoke for Honourable Baskota, the member from Kholawari district on the other side of the Karnali, who was his personal friend and his wife's brother-in-law. They had been married to two sisters. Mr Baskota had been married for seven years but had no children. He had therefore decided to wed a new bride who would bear him a son. This was allowed by law in Nepal, provided that the first wife was infertile. A doctor had to certify that the wife was truly infertile and the report had to be registered with the Chief District Officer (CDO). I immediately understood the need for the presence of the Governor, the boss of the CDO. I was sure that the two thugs had asked him to support their demand of me. It was clear that I was being ordered to certify Mrs Baskota as infertile so that her husband could remarry. I did not like being manipulated in this way and began to think of ways to avoid such an unethical action. I was not obliged to give any certificate like this and could decline to do so.

I thought of referring them to the consultant gynaecologist in Nepalgunj, a mere twenty minutes away by plane, but it was necessary to do this in a patient manner. I began to probe gently.

Being a public figure, it was essential that the Honourable Baskota was seen to be observing the law. Keeping as neutral a face as possible, I enquired whether he had found a new bride already. Mr Giri said that they wished to keep all this within the family and so Mrs Baskota's younger sister had agreed to this marriage. She was twenty years old and had been living with Mr Giri and his wife for some months, preparing for the School Leaving Certificate (SLC) which was due to be held the following month.

Mr Baskota was over fifty years old; a rich and powerful broker in

Kathmandu. Both he and his friend Mr Giri were rumoured to be involved with drugs and the theft of old idols of archaeological importance from the temples. It was also said that they shared the proceeds with the King. I was in no doubt that they could harm me and my family with impunity.

I cautioned myself to refuse the request at my peril. It is indeed an art to appear to agree to everything at first and then to take advantage of the situation when your opponent has dropped his guard. This trick had served me and Leela well over the years. I hoped to find a way out of this new predicament if I could have a frank discussion with the ladies in question.

'You know I need to observe a few formalities in cases like this. I take it that Mrs Baskota has agreed to this arrangement,' I said. There was vigorous head nodding in the affirmative. I continued, 'Please send her to the hospital tomorrow afternoon so that she can be examined and the formalities can be completed. Should I get the certificate registered at the CDO office or would you prefer to collect it from me?'

'I shall send my secretary on Monday to collect it. Could it be typed and ready by then?' asked Mr Baskota.

'Oh yes. Monday will be fine,' I assured him.

I continued to appear obliging. 'Perhaps she could be accompanied by her young sister? Maybe we should also examine her to make sure that there is nothing preventing her from conceiving in due course. It will be such a waste of your valuable time and effort, Honourable Baskotaji, to marry a sterile bride once again,' I said.

The two Honourables looked at each other and decided to stop whatever they were about to say. They declined a second glass of tea and departed, well satisfied.

My mind was racing. Giving a false medical certificate was unethical but perhaps I could justify this somewhat by claiming mortal danger to myself and my family. It could be seen as an attempt at self-preservation, which is ethical.

'Don't fool yourself, Prasanna,' said my soul. 'Do you realise that by this action of yours, an innocent woman will be treated worse than a slave? In due course she may also lose all her property rights, and be made destitute. Can you live with that?' I was challenged. I had to find a better way.

I began discreetly to ask questions about the people involved. I managed to get the picture piece by piece. Mr Baskota had already been married twice. His first wife had run away with a Tibetan trader selling *yarchegumba,* a herb that grows above seventeen thousand feet and has proven aphrodisiac properties. Mr Baskota naturally had felt humiliated. To hide his shame, he had married a much younger bride within a few months. This had proved costly as he had had to write off the substantial loan which he had previously given to the father of the bride. The poor girl had been forced to marry someone nearly thirty years older than herself. I was still curious. I could not establish the connection with Mr Giri in this affair. Traditional Nepalese sons-in-law rarely get involved in the affairs of the relatives of their wives. Neither could I understand why the two older sisters wished the young girl to be married to this old man. Their father had no more debts to pay and was apparently doing well. I sensed that there were things about which they had not told me.

The three sisters, Thuli, Maili and Mitthu, arrived the following afternoon. It was a bit of a surprise as I was not expecting Thuli (Mrs Giri) also to come. She was big, buxom, loud and imperious. She took control of the meeting. When I asked, she explained that she was like the son that her father had never had and that she had three much younger half-sisters. The youngest, Maiya, was looking after their father in the village of Seenja, three days' walk away. He was not very well and would not be attending the wedding. The step-mother was busy and would not attend either.

She explained that it was her decision for Mitthu to marry Mr Baskota. Mitthu was childish and easily led astray. Going to the home of her older sister as a new bride would provide her with extra security, she reasoned. I asked if she did not think that Mr Baskota was too old. 'Not really,' she said. 'What is fifty-six years for a man? My own father married for the second time at fifty-eight and our youngest sister, Maiya, is now already seventeen. Moreover, Maiya also needs to be married. Our father is not keeping good health and is not so rich as to be able to find young, rich boys for Mitthu and Maiya.'

'I see. I need to talk with Mrs Baskota first, and then get Mitthu examined by Dr Leela,' I said.

I looked at Maili, Mrs Baskota, who was soon to be certified as sterile. Her eyes were aflame with anger; her body was taut and her face tensed in a grimace. Aged about twenty-four, she was beautiful and her curves showed in spite of being wrapped modestly in a brown shawl and sari. I asked Thuli to go to Dr Leela for a chat, and to take Mitthu with her. Thuli was worried as Mitthu was being troubled by '*Khola ko Bhuut*' ('the Spirit of the Mountain Stream') and was unwell.

The Spirit was a wicked one. It would make a young maiden vomit and faint, and cause her stomach to bloat. Only a local *jhankri* (similar to a witch doctor) could get rid of the Spirit. We had treated a few women with incomplete abortions, who had sworn their innocence and blamed the Spirit. I suggested that Dr Leela should see Mitthu, who was covered in a long black cloak with a hood over her head, the traditional winter garb of women in that area. I could hardly see her face.

They left us to the confrontation I had been dreading, for I knew not what to expect. Maili let out a long breath.

'How dare you certify me sterile, you slave of the Honourable? I too can give you money. Will you certify the Honourable to be the one with the problem?' A torrent of scathing words flowed from her mouth, unleashing her suppressed anger and frustration. 'You call yourself a doctor. Do doctors behave like this?' she hissed. I had not suspected that I was the cause of her anger.

I raised my hand and said sternly, 'Enough. If I wanted to certify you sterile, I would have done so yesterday. Why do you think that I called you today?'

It took a moment for her to assimilate what I had said. Suspiciously, she retorted, 'Why have you called me then? I am not sterile.'

'Why don't you start by telling me the problem? Maybe I can help,' I suggested quietly.

She was silent for a while, and then began to weep copious tears from those beautiful eyes, beating her chest and cursing the day she was born. Abruptly, she stood up and came to me, grabbing my hand. 'Feel my breasts. Tell me, are these the breasts of a sterile woman?' she challenged, pressing my hand onto her bosom.

'Are they not full of milk that I have never had a chance to give? My god knows that all my life I have yearned to suckle a baby.' It was most disconcerting. She had a strong grip and I struggled to push her away.

'Get a hold of yourself, Mrs Baskota,' I said, the worst thing one can say to an agitated person, but I was young and naïve then. She became like someone possessed.

'You ask me to get a hold of myself. How should I do that? Can you give me the hot rod that that husband of mine has never given me? Are you man enough to do so?' Suddenly she was grabbing at my crotch. I jumped up and fell backwards over the chair. She found that amusing and started to laugh hysterically.

I scrambled up and asked, 'Are you a virgin, then?' The laughing abruptly stopped. She wiped her tears and rearranged her shawl. Once composed, she sat down opposite me.

'Yes,' she whispered, 'He has never touched me. He blackens his face with boys in Kathmandu. I have never looked at another man. I have been faithful to him. Now he wants to humiliate me publicly by certifying me sterile.' Again, she started sobbing uncontrollably. IVF was not known in those days. Artificial insemination was restricted to cows only. A discarded wife was no prize for any man. The woman would be doomed socially.

Things were beginning to get a little clearer but I was still far from getting the whole picture. I did not understand why she would agree to her younger sister being subjected to the same hell as herself. I asked her so. Before she could answer, Leela opened the door and beckoned for me to join her in the corridor.

'*Bhuut* (the Spirit) is at it again,' she whispered. 'He has made her eight weeks pregnant.' I stood there trying to figure out this new revelation. All at once it became very clear. I smiled. Mr Giri was a rogue and Mr Baskota was gay. Mrs Giri was desperately trying to make the pregnancy of her younger sister look legitimate by getting her married to a homosexual. The only one to lose out in this game plan was poor Maili. I had to help her. 'They don't call you a wily so-and-so for nothing, Honourable Giriji,' I muttered to myself, smiling as I re-entered the room.

Maili was much calmer and had stopped sobbing. I asked whether she knew about her sister and the Spirit. She did not know and said that she did not care. Thuli was obviously a tight-lipped woman who would give orders and not explanations. In a flash, I thought of a solution.

'I will help you. Do as I say,' I said to her. She nodded. Resigned and exhausted, she had nothing more to lose. I explained my suggestion to her. It had something to do with the Spirit of the Mountain Stream near her father's village. Hindu scriptures have many instances of chaste wives being impregnated by gods when their husbands had been unable to do so. At first she would not agree but when I pointed out to her that certificate or not, her husband would get married again, she agreed to carry out the plan. She knew that the alternative of simply submitting was to invite disaster into her life. She allowed Leela to examine her. Her hymen was intact.

'Sometimes it so happens that the older wife also becomes pregnant soon after the new wife conceives,' I said to no-one in particular. They had re-assembled in my consulting room and the session had come to an end. Thuli, the wise matriarch, looked at me hard and instantly agreed.

'Life and death are not in our hands are they, doctor? We've got to grin and bear it,' she sighed and prepared to leave. 'We still need your certificate, Doctor *Saheb*,' she said with finality.

'I once certified that a woman could not conceive. Six months later, she too became pregnant along with the second wife. The second wife produced a daughter but the first wife had a son. How embarrassing it was for me. The poor man spent all that money and got married again for nothing.' I spun the yarn for the benefit of the nursing assistant and the two orderlies who were within earshot.

Monday came. Honourable Baskota himself came to get the certificate. Clearly, he was most curious. He looked hard at my face searching for an answer to the question he dare not ask. I let him squirm. I suggested that it would be best if he sent Maili to her father at Seenja. She was very stressed and should not be allowed to be present at his marriage. He agreed, keen to avoid confrontation. I suggested that he get married quietly and without overt ceremony. He agreed. He took the certificate and was about to go when one of the orderlies said loudly, 'It happened in Mugu, Sir.' When asked to explain, he blurted out how a first wife had become pregnant after the *sauta* (second wife) had conceived. He had been desperately trying to remember the place where he had heard the story and had suddenly remembered. Mr Baskota hastily retreated.

Maili came to see me before going to the village of her childhood. I loudly told her to stay there as long as it took for her father to get better. She understood that I meant her to return as soon as she got pregnant, having sought out the Spirit. 'May your trip be successful,' I said. She looked at me gratefully, attempted to touch my feet in reverence, and hid her face sobbing. Mitthu was married the following week.

Many months later, Leela and I were invited by Mr Giri for dinner. He had returned from Kathmandu when the House went into recess, and wanted me to taste the cider he had made during the last monsoon. There was also the matter of settling our fee, which was nine months overdue. Mr Baskota had not paid us and had left it to his friend to settle the account.

The meal was excellent. We were given *danfe* (an exotic, rare, pheasant), wild boar and fresh vegetables. It was a lavish spread, washed down with the cider, which was indeed very good. A pretty young girl was helping Thuli to serve us.

Leela asked her *'Baini, timro nam ke ho?'* ('Sister, what is your name?')

'This is my youngest sister, Maiya,' said Thuli. 'She just arrived today. She will be studying for the SLC examination.' Honourable Giri's roving eyes were openly admiring this innocent young girl. I knew that I had to prevent another disaster.

When the time to depart approached, Honourable Giri took out his wallet and asked me what our fee was. I said that we would waive our fees if Mr Giri could help us with our family planning campaign in the region. He said that he would gladly assist us and asked what he would have to do. I told him, with assurances that his public image would greatly benefit. The prospect of fame seemed to make him willing. He insisted on paying us generously.

We had publicised the inaugural meeting widely. A large crowd gathered in a field to the north of our out-patient building. Among other dignitaries, His Excellency the Governor graced the occasion. Honourable Baskota inaugurated the zonal office of the Family Planning and Maternal and Child Health Project that afternoon. We had three volunteers to help with the event. The Honourable Member of *Rastria Panchayat*, Mr Giri, was the first volunteer to have a vasectomy. I came out after performing the operation, watched by many men, and announced that the regular clinic would start from the next day.

Mrs Mitthu Baskota proudly held a beautiful baby daughter of three months. She had been the first patient in the district to have been delivered by a trained midwife at home.

Mrs Maili Baskota was pregnant, seven years after her marriage. She was the first in the queue for an antenatal check-up. I was sure that the Governor's spies would not have been able to discover the true identity of the Spirit of the Mountain Stream. Maili had secretly spread the rumour that it was, in fact, the Honourable Baskota himself.

SECTION II
Dharan

CHAPTER 11

Never Again

It was a hot summer afternoon in Dharan; everyone was trying to take a siesta or rest in the cool shade. Out of nowhere a horde of men and women came rushing to the hospital. Buried within this crowd were four men who were bringing a patient to be treated.

Dharan is at the foothills of the eastern mountains of Nepal. It is the gateway to Dhankuta and beyond. At the time Leela and I worked there, between 1974 and 1977, it was a violent town of about one hundred thousand people. The British had a recruitment centre for Gurkha soldiers at nearby Ghopa camp. The Government hospital, where we worked, was a small fifteen-bedded unit, manned by three doctors and a few nurses. The ethnicity of Dharan's population varied widely, but the *Rai* and *Limbu* clans were more visible than the rest. Perhaps this was due to the clan youth, who would frequently pick fights, intimidate each other and indulge in gang warfare. The senior clansmen were steeped in tradition and would defend their honour by drawing their *khukri* (curved knives) and attacking their enemies at the drop of a hat.

We had always to be ready to repair and dress the wounds that resulted when these fights broke out. Most of the time, however, the hospital was relatively peaceful but very busy. Thankfully, we had until this time had no threats to our personal safety. Two of our predecessors had been forced to flee the town under cover of darkness, fearing for their lives after being attacked. I still do not know the reason fully but it had something to do with charging very high fees.

The younger generation in Dharan used to be rather demanding of us, not docile and disciplined like their elders. However, the hospital and the local youth had a good relationship, largely thanks to Leela. They gave her great respect. She had managed to make them all her own 'brothers and sisters'. Some had started to volunteer to help in the out-patient clinics, giving them a little respectability in the eyes of the town. In reality, they were there to find any excuse they could to cause trouble.

(The township, with its hospital, was badly damaged by an earthquake in 1979 and has been largely rebuilt. It has grown enormously over the years.)

It had been a peaceful and calm afternoon until that moment. The out-patient clinic had been unusually heavy during the morning. Two of the patients on the ward were very unstable. I had been yo-yo-ing between the in-patient and out-patient blocks, all the while trying to talk with a large number of relatives who seemed to follow my every movement. The work had stretched well beyond the usual time, eventually settling down by about three PM.

I was dozing after a late lunch. The whirring table fan was puffing cool humid air at me, producing a soporific effect. The commotion outside my ground-floor flat woke me up. I looked out of the window. The hospital courtyard was crowded with approximately one hundred people in a state of great excitement. A wounded man was just about visible in the midst of the throng. The people around him appeared to be protecting him from a larger group of men carrying *khukri*, sickles and sticks, who were shouting threats of slaughter. The patient's protectors were tramping over large blotches of blood that had fallen from him, but they appeared to be unaware of this.

This looked ominous. Why was an angry mob in a hospital? I rushed out and went to the Emergency Room. The hospital porter and the guard at the gate had the presence of mind to take the patient quickly inside and shut the door forcibly, thus keeping the unruly crowd at bay. The so-called Emergency Room was a small room with an examination couch, a few instruments, syringes, hypodermic needles, bandages and other such equipment. At best, it served to provide first aid and deal with minor cuts, bruises and simple fractures.

The patient was crying with pain, clutching at his genitals with his hand, which was smeared with blood. The four men who had brought him in were standing in a corner of the room. I looked at them inquisitively and was informed that the man's wife had whacked his *saman* (penis) with a *khunda* (cleaver).

The patient, Ram, was a *Limbu* smallholder who never did any work. He had returned a few years before after a stint in the Indian Army and bought a few acres of land. He had married the pretty daughter of a poor peasant from a nearby village. His wife had known of his infidelities but had tolerated them with innate dignity and because of social pressure. They had two young children. Ram spent his time playing cards and *carom*, a popular board game, with his friends, smoking ganja and womanising. His wife had come back from the fields earlier than usual that day.

What she had witnessed in their bedroom had been unbearable. The woman was a neighbour and not even as pretty or as young as herself. She and Ram were naked, lying on her bed and enjoying themselves. She had caught them in the act. It must have been too much for her to tolerate calmly. She had first caught the woman by her hair and dragged her naked into the street. She could not kick her enough. A small crowd gathered very quickly. Shouting loud obscenities, she would probably have killed the woman with her kicks and blows had some of the people in the crowd not intervened.

The wife had then returned, gone into the cowshed, where all the agricultural implements were stored, and picked up a large cleaver to sever the genitalia of her husband. She had almost succeeded. After all, she was a *Limbu* woman and had every right to defend her honour. She was not just a pretty face. I suspected that only a few in the crowd who were demanding revenge were men from her father's clan. Many were not connected; the excitement simply provided a good excuse for a fight.

Ram's friends and the two porters helped me to undress him. I began examining the wounds while one of the men told me the story.

They were all laughing. Ram was not in physical shock, in spite of having lost a lot of blood. He was obviously shaken and cringing with shame. Whether due to the irritation caused by several abrasions to the shaft of his penis or to the fear and excitement of it all, he was still in arousal. Luckily for him, his penile shaft had not been severed. However, the wound was quite deep and bleeding profusely. There were deep cuts on his buttocks, the back of one hand, his face and his shoulder. Some of these were still bleeding. It was clear that in her rage his wife had started with his penis and then hit him at random with the cleaver thereafter.

He needed to be taken to our small operating theatre so that I could try to salvage his penis and sew up the other wounds. This meant taking him outside and wheeling him thirty yards through the crowd to the in-patient block – a daunting prospect with the mob baying for revenge. I administered first aid and set up a drip. We put gauze pieces over the main wound and pressed at the bleeding points to gain some control over the situation. A shot of pethidine intramuscularly helped Ram to calm down a little and probably gave some pain relief. I looked outside at the angry throng.

The crowd had already doubled. Suddenly there was more commotion. The husband of the other woman had found out about his wife's infidelity. He had started by hitting and kicking her in the face. Then he had decided that his honour would be salvaged if he chopped off her lover's head in front of her. He would then cut off her head as well. He had dragged her to the hospital for this purpose and was demanding the culprit come out into the open. He was furiously brandishing a large *khukri*. He was a *Rai*.

Generally, the *Rai* and *Limbu*, often known collectively as *Kiranti*, are gentle and devout people. However, they are well known to have a very short fuse. As I have already said, they produce their *khukri* at the slightest provocation. It was once said that it would be unthinkable for a true *Kiranti* to put the *khukri* back in its scabbard unless it had spilled some blood. This cuckold had had more than a minor provocation to do just that. He was impatient, shouting challenges and threats, jumping several feet in the air and stamping his feet.

Some women in the crowd managed to pull the unfaithful wife away from her irate husband. She too was now bleeding and significantly injured. Luckily for her, the big Murari, our auxiliary health worker, and the hospital porter were able to carry her. They moved her into the Emergency Room, thereby bringing both the culprits together. The mob was now openly demanding their heads. Something had to be done quickly to avert the bloodshed, but what?

Crowd control and public relations were not in our curriculum as medical students. I heard a voice demanding that the doctor be beaten as well for hiding the culprits. I was now sure that it was just a matter of time before the mob turned on us as well. My five-year-old son and wife were exposed along with me and we had no protection whatsoever. The two porters and big Murari were vulnerable too. How was I to avoid this disaster? What was to be done?

I came out of the Emergency Room and, standing on the raised platform of a Peepul tree, squarely faced the heaving crowd. More people were still coming in from the street. A lull fell over the throng. They were clearly expecting me to give them all the details. Raised hands were still raised. Mouths shouting incitement were still open. I sensed imminent and grave danger.

On a sudden impulse, I shouted as loudly as I could that they must clear off the premises at once, or else. Did they have no sense of decorum? I said that other patients were being disturbed and that the police were on their way. Did they have no pride? It was a quarrel between a husband and wife; were they not ashamed to interfere?

I saw one young man in his twenties standing in the crowd with a few of his friends. He was a ring-leader in his *Rai* community. This was an opportune moment for them to create further trouble. He was about to say something to his friends, who appeared to have sticks and knives at the ready, when he caught my eye. He was the son of a retired British Gurkha soldier, whom Leela had made her 'brother'. Pointing a finger at him, I said, '*Kiran Bhai, la iniharulai bhagaunus yahyan bata. Latti le hane pani huncha, manenan bhane.*' ('Brother Kiran, get these people out of here. You may kick them if necessary.') The mob was not expecting the ferocity in my voice. Their moment of hesitation allowed the *Rai* youths to group together. These youths, who were always looking for a fight, could now attack the crowd with my blessings. They would be doing so to save the hospital. The crowd probably thought that Kiran and his friends were under my control. Not wishing to be involved with either the police or the *Rai* boys, they drifted out quietly and disappeared into the street. Only the cuckold husband and cheated wife remained, still shouting obscenities. Kiran and his friends stayed as guards inside the hospital gate. Leela and Nandan then came out of the flat. Kiran and his friends greeted her saying, '*Namaste, didi*' ('Greetings, sister'). Leela took care of the injured unfaithful wife whilst Nandan went to play with Kiran. The porters were able to take Ram to the operating theatre.

It was all peaceful and normal once again, thanks to my false bravado. I had managed to split the crowd and deflected a potential attack. The relief was unbelievable. It was my turn to start shaking. I desperately needed to hold onto something and sit down, but my pride would not allow it.

What would I have done if my shouting had not done the trick?

CHAPTER 12

A Cervical Grip

'Not a mark!' exclaimed Nirmala, the midwife.

Elated, I struggled in vain to look serious. The midwife was unaware that I had never before used forceps to deliver a baby without expert supervision or assistance. Yet it had turned out to be a near perfect application. It was pure fluke!

'Thank you,' I said, looking at the newborn. There was nothing more than a faint line over one cheek, which would not bruise. The baby was pink and moving all his limbs; a beautiful baby boy. He cried weakly at first, more like the meow of a disorientated kitten, but naturally his wails became louder and more piercing in protest. He had been unceremoniously grabbed by the head and hauled from the comfort of his mother's warm womb. He made fists in the air and screamed loudly again.

'I do not think he is thanking me,' I thought.

'Welcome to our world,' I said to him.

Nirmala knew that I had many patients waiting and offered to finish up with the baby and his mother. Grateful for this support, I hurried back to the out-patient clinic.

I had been called in to help only a little while before because Indramaya, a girl of barely sixteen, had not been able to deliver her baby spontaneously. It was her first pregnancy. She had arrived at the hospital about an hour earlier after over two days spent in labour. The village midwife could not cope and in desperation had set her on a bullock cart to journey twenty-five miles to our hospital. The agonising screams of each contraction had heralded her arrival.

Nirmala had examined the poor girl and started an intravenous infusion of dextrose solution to help with blood pressure and general well-being. Once the contractions had slowed down, exhaustion consumed her and her sobs of pain diminished. Her blood pressure was low but the heart rate of her unborn baby was satisfactory. Its head had crowned nicely so we could see it in the birth canal but the mother just could not push. Nirmala therefore decided that outlet forceps would be necessary to assist the birth.

I was busy in the out-patient clinic when Nirmala came to explain the situation. Both Leela and Pushpa, the other two doctors at the hospital, were away from Dharan that day. Leela usually looked after the obstetrics and gynaecology patients. I would assist her when she needed help. I did all the routine medical work. Pushpa, being the senior doctor, a chest specialist with a huge private practice, saw mostly chest patients and dealt with hospital administration. On this occasion I was on my own.

Nirmala was a highly trained and experienced midwife. If it had not been for her, Leela would never have been able to cope with the workload. So I had no reason to doubt her assessment. The trouble was that I had never conducted a delivery with forceps.

En route to the labour room, my mind was rapidly delving into the deep recesses of my brain trying to recall all the information I had memorised about forceps delivery. It was sheer coincidence that this had been the subject of my final-year obstetric viva exam five years before. First, the examiner had asked me what the indications were for deciding to use forceps. When I had blurted out all the relevant conditions, she had asked me to identify the correct instrument from among several gadgets laid out in front of her on her huge desk. I had picked up the forceps and held each half in either hand.

'Go on, apply the blades,' she had instructed, pushing a latex pelvis towards me. I did as requested and locked the blades.

'Now pull out the baby,' she had said.

The textbook procedure was to use both hands, first down, then towards you, and then up towards your chest in a smooth half elliptical arc. I did just that, to the smiles of the examiner. I later discovered that she had given me the highest marks for that viva voce examination. Now, five years later, I needed to be certain that I had retained these textbook skills.

'Can you do this in real life?' asked a frightened, untrained young doctor of himself. I had no choice but to try it and find out.

I could see that Nirmala had made an accurate assessment. Unfortunately, I also found that the baby's heart rate had begun to slow down. There was no time to send our patient fifty miles to the obstetrician at Biratnagar Hospital. We had not a moment to lose if the baby was to be saved. I washed, gloved and gowned, and perched on a stool facing the birth canal like an expert. I must have appeared to be a confident, experienced obstetrician about to perform a routine forceps delivery. In truth I was shaking in my sandals and silently praying to every deity that I could remember. First down, then towards me, and then up I rehearsed silently. Miraculously, the procedure was a success. The gods must have guided my hands.

I left Nirmala to continue with the rest of the delivery and hurried back to out-patients. The joy of conducting a normal routine delivery is exquisite. The fact that I had been able to intervene with forceps in the nick of time and save the baby made me feel like bursting with joy. I wanted to shout from the rooftops, to sing and dance, to celebrate. But I had to control all these emotions and focus on the rest of my work. It was a hot day in May. I bore the heat until I had finished with the last of the out-patients. It was then time to look at the patients on the ward before going for lunch.

It was past one PM. I was beginning to feel hungry and hoping the ward round would not take too long. A cold glass of beer while waiting for food to be served would be most appropriate and welcome, I thought to myself. Fate, however, had other plans in store.

Nirmala appeared again. She had given Indramaya one shot of

ergometrine, a drug which helps the placenta to separate from the inside of the womb after birth, but nothing had happened. She had tried gently pulling on the umbilical cord and had put her hand inside but had been unable to feel any point of separation. Meanwhile, the new mother was still bleeding. Nirmala wanted me to assess the patient and perhaps remove the placenta by hand. (No part of the placenta, or 'after-birth' should remain in the mother or there is a risk of haemorrhage and infection.)

Aside from a brief internship in a busy labour room, I had had very little obstetrics experience. All I could do with confidence was perform episiotomies (a small cut to widen the birth canal to let the baby through more easily) and suture them again very well. I could not remember ever having removed a placenta by hand. I did not know how. But I did not tell Nirmala. What would be the point?

'Can we send her to Biratnagar Hospital?' I asked hopefully.

'Not really. Her people have left,' she explained. 'The farmer with the bullock cart has had to go back to his village for some urgent business. Her mother-in-law is here but we have no transport to send her to Biratnagar. We will have to do whatever we can here.'

Back to the labour room I went again. I saw poor Indramaya, now totally exhausted, looking pale and with a rapid weak pulse. She was bleeding profusely and nearly in shock. I changed the infusion drip to a normal saline. Donning a pair of gloves I examined her. The opening to her womb, her cervix, was still open. The stump of the umbilical cord was hanging out whilst its far end disappeared inside. When I squeezed her womb from above with both hands about an ounce of dark blood came out. This was not a good sign.

I was making these observations with only half my brain. The other half was desperately trying to remember the causes of non-separation of the placenta, and of post-birth haemorrhage, and how to treat them. I was sure that I could not operate. I had to find a way to treat her medically and mechanically. What was I supposed to do?

I gave her one more shot of ergometrine, then scrubbed, gowned and gloved once again. Very gently, I inserted my hand into her womb. I felt all over for a breach in the placental attachment but could not find one. The inside surface was without a break. Then something gripped my wrist as though to prevent me exploring any further. I realised her cervix was beginning to contract though her womb was still flaccid. If I removed my hand, the cervix would close and all the blood would accumulate inside while the placenta remained still firmly attached. The woman would surely die. This likely chain of events flashed through my mind. I was close to panicking.

'Oh Dantakali, guide my hand', I prayed silently.

The cervical grip over my wrist had become quite firm. I decided to give the patient a third shot of ergometrine in the hope that her womb would somehow finally contract. It could be a dangerous drug with horrible toxic effects but I could think of no other drug that would stimulate the womb in such a manner. I felt that I had no choice. I kept my hand inside and waited. About five minutes later I decided to dig gently with my fingers along the placental border. At last I found a breach. I inserted my little finger and gently advanced it into the gap; carefully I began to break the adhesions. I was also gently pressing on the body of the womb from above with my left hand.

The patient's cervix now responded more violently, gripping my right wrist like a vice. My fingers, however, were still mobile, and this was all I cared about at that moment. I continued. My little finger began to hurt. My hand started to get mild cramp. But I had to continue until the entire placenta had been separated. It took a long time. At last, I could no longer feel any part still adhering to the inside of the womb. The placenta must have separated entirely. That was a great relief but now I had to get the whole thing out quickly or it would complicate matters even further.

I grabbed as much of the placenta as I could and tried to pull my fist out of the body of the womb. It was impossible. The cervix had become too tight and narrow. I tried gently increasing the force with which I pulled, yet still there was no give. I had to let go of the placenta and barely managed to pull my hand out. The cervix was closing up before my eyes.

The umbilical cord provided a little hold and, hoping that it would not snap, I began to pull at it gently. Slowly, very very slowly, it brought with it the placenta. I examined it to check that it was whole and that no part had been left behind to cause further trouble. It had a few raw surfaces over some of its segments from where the structures that had anchored it had been so deeply embedded in the wall of the womb that they had broken off. The problem appeared to be only partial and not to affect the whole placenta. I breathed a sigh of relief. If it had been a 'complete placenta accreta' the patient would have needed a hysterectomy. 'She should not bleed much any more. Leela can assess her tomorrow,' I told Nirmala, wiping my brow with the folds of my surgical gown. I started to massage my wrist. I could never have imagined that a cervix could grip with that intensity. Indramaya was lying almost comatose with exhaustion and relief. The baby was neatly tucked away in a small cot. He was not shouting or making fists now that he was reconciled to his predicament. All was peaceful. Nirmala beamed at me again. A young mother had been saved.

My legs were shaking and I felt totally drained. I still had the ward round to do. I walked out towards the in-patient block. The cold beer would have to wait.

CHAPTER 13

Sister Tara

'Tara *Didi* (Sister) is dying, Doctor *saheb*. You need to hurry,' said the young man who had been sent to fetch me. This news came as a shock to us. Just two days before I had checked her blood pressure and had found it well controlled.

Once the doctor-patient professional formalities had been completed, Srimati Chapagain had reverted to being the universally liked and revered Tara Didi and quietly slipped inside our small flat. Ignoring the only chair, stuffed with the day's washing, she had made herself comfortable on our bed, sitting cross-legged. It was the norm for intimate friends and relatives to enter the bedroom and sit on the bed. She had had a cup of tea with Leela, who was recovering from an illness, and played with Nandan. I had left them chatting and gone about my work.

Hastily swallowing the last morsel of my lunch, I rushed to wash my hands. (One ate with ones fingers; the use of cutlery was not common in those days.) The young man continued, 'She has been brought outside and laid in the front quadrangle in the open. The *jyotishiji* (astrologer) has said that it would be auspicious to die now. All her relatives have already arrived.'

Drying my hands I asked, 'Who sent you to fetch me?'

'Bharat,' he said. Bharat was an orphan whom Tara had brought up as her own child. He was about sixteen years old. She used to call him *nati* (grandson) as she was too old to call him son. She did not have any children of her own. Bharat too was very much attached to the old lady.

I continued to talk with the young man while picking up my bag. Then we set off with him sitting on the rear seat of my motor cycle, holding the bag on his knees. Tara lived towards the eastern end of Dharan. Her house was by the main road, which was quite steep in segments. My 50cc bike had difficulty in carrying both of us. At times we had to get off and push until the gradient became less steep. At other times, only I could manage and the young man would walk. We pressed on, although our progress was rather slow.

Tara Didi was a lady of immense personality. Her father had been a very learned man and teacher in Itahari, a small township nearby. He had taught Tara and her sister and brother. Tara knew how to read and write well. She could recite many prayers verbatim. She had read the *Ramayana, Mahabharat* and many stories from the *Puranas* by the time she was married, aged eight, to the youngest son of a rich landlord in Dharan.

Her young husband, aged ten years, had died rather suddenly during an outbreak of cholera the year after the marriage. Two years later, her parents sent her to the house of her late husband in Dharan. The tradition in those days demanded that she would have her first menstruation in her husband's house.

She was not made welcome. The in-laws allowed her to remain until she had had her first period. They planned then to send her back to the house of her father after the twelfth day of purification.

She may have been a child but the courage she showed would shame many older girls. She refused to be sent back. She maintained that the house of her husband was her rightful home. Her two mothers-in-law and three older sisters-in-law were resentful of her. As a widow remaining faithful to her husband, she stood to inherit a quarter of the vast family property. These women and her father-in-law wanted to get her out of the way for good. She began to be treated badly. She was ordered to do all the menial chores in the house.

Those were the days of the Rana regime in Nepal. The whole of Nepal was like a huge estate owned by the Ranas. The King of Nepal was merely a figurehead. The Prime Minister and his brothers were the rulers. They dominated all Nepalese people, whom they treated as their tenants. They used to appoint Bailiffs who had power equivalent to a magistrate or a district judge. These men appeared fair in their judgements as long as disputes did not threaten their rule, interests and traditions.

The story was that, unknown to her in-laws, Tara sent a written petition to the Bailiff. Her father-in-law was not too pleased when he received a summons from the court. In court Tara answered all the questions herself. Her father-in-law denied on oath that she was being ill-treated. He promised to look after his young daughter-in-law. Tara was told to complain again if she had any more trouble. One can only guess what must have subsequently happened in that household.

Widows were treated worse than women whose husbands were alive. They were not allowed to re-marry. Nor were they allowed to come to the fore on auspicious occasions such as weddings. They were required to hide their faces early in the morning as it was believed that seeing the face of a widow first thing meant inviting a disastrous misfortune that day. As a young woman of eighteen Tara used to ride to her fields and supervise the workers. No gentlewoman was supposed to be seen in public without a maid, or a veil, and certainly not on horseback with a rifle on the saddle. This was heavily frowned upon in those days. It was now the turn of her brothers-in-law to take her to court.

She was summoned to a superior court of the District Commissioner, who was the cousin of the Prime Minister, Chandra Sumshere Rana. The Commissioner must have been startled by Tara's beauty hidden within the white garb of a widow. When asked why she disrupted the social norms, she is said to have replied, 'There is no law preventing women from looking after their own estate. I would lose everything and starve if I did not look after my own property.' The District Commissioner is supposed to have made a flippant remark to the effect that she should keep a man to service all her needs. She understood the innuendo and shouted, 'How dare you suggest defiling a Brahmin widow? If you have the courage, make a law that will allow widows to remarry. Then I will find a husband who will pay your taxes and teach you how to respect a lady.'

Even a Rana District Commissioner could not stand up to her challenge and the case was dismissed.

As she grew older she developed into a highly spiritual person with great inner strength. She would never mince her words and no-one could silence her when she spoke for a cause. She was the champion of the weak.

Then came the revolution of 1950 when Tara is supposed to have shot many soldiers single-handed. That had been twenty-four years before, when she was forty years old. Dharan had been liberated from the Rana occupation. Unfortunately, social emancipation had not followed political enlightenment. Tara represented the rebellion of suppressed womanhood in rural Nepal, where women continued to be treated as personal possessions. She had become Tara Didi (Sister Tara) to all but was not recognised by the political leaders as the great pioneer that she was. Perhaps this was because she did not join any political group. Such was the forceful personality of Tara Didi that all women loved her.

What a great loss to Nepal, I thought. She was a living legend, a pioneer of social reform, a beacon of hope for millions of suppressed women. And she was dying, aged only sixty-four years. But Bharat thought that I might be able to do something. What could I do? My heart began to sink at the sound of loud hymns accompanied by the din of *tabla* (drums) and a wailing harmonium. Had she died already? We reached her house to find hundreds of people had gathered. I had to push them aside to reach her. Then I saw a sight that I shall never forget.

It was a bright, warm afternoon. A courtyard of some forty yards square, surrounded on all four sides by the main house, an animal shed, a cook house and the guest quarters, was packed with people except at the centre. There, right in the middle, was a heap of flowers and garlands, beside which sat an unknown old woman dressed in a white sari who periodically seemed to be putting a little water to the flowers. Respectfully sitting a few feet away were the musicians with their harmoniums, *tablas*, *binas* and *mridangas*. Some had hand-held brass percussion instruments. They were singing devotional songs accompanied by the un-orchestrated musical notes. All were creating an atmosphere of great sorrow and melancholy. I looked around to find Bharat hurrying towards me. Together we walked towards the heap of flowers.

'Let her go peacefully, doctor. You are not needed now,' said an authoritative voice. It was one of her several nephews. He attempted to block my approach. I returned his *namaste* and smiled, pretending that he had just greeted me. I continued to walk forward. Only Tara Didi's face was visible. She appeared to be asleep. The rest of her body was fully covered by flowers and garlands. I knelt beside her and looked at her intently while searching for her pulse.

It is considered a sacrilege by orthodox Hindus for an unclean person to touch a dying Brahmin who has just been purified by the waters from all the four holy places. Everything appeared to have been done to ensure that Tara's soul would travel to the land of the gods. She was wet so I assumed that she had been bathed and wrapped in a fresh shroud. She was being fed *Ganga jal,* the holy water from the Ganges, as the last act of sustenance for her final journey. My irreverent act was of such magnitude that it stopped all the music and hymn singing. There was an ominous silence.

How dare this doctor cause such sacrilege? One hundred pairs of hostile eyes were demanding my obedience.

Bharat started to sob in between telling me that Tara had suddenly complained of a severe headache while sipping a cup of tea. She had clutched the back of her neck and then keeled over. She had rolled her eyes upwards and started to froth at the mouth. He had panicked and raised the alarm. A *baidyaji* (a traditional ayurvedic practitioner) who lived nearby had come instantly. He had felt her pulse and shaken his head. She did not have much time left he had said.

It was his advice to take her outside into the open so that she could go to heaven. He had then departed, stopping at the house of the family priest en route. The priest had come running and managed to perform the last rites in time. He had alerted the *jyotishiji* (astrologer) who had also arrived in haste with his bundle of almanacs and charts.

He had calculated the celestial configuration and pronounced that this was an auspicious time to die. All this had happened before Bharat could send for me.

Tara's pulse was strong but slow. Her lips and the insides of her eyelids were pink. She moaned softly when I pressed hard on her breast bone. Her blood pressure was elevated. I moved towards her feet and uncovered them. Her toes were pink. Both the big toes turned up when I stroked the soles of her feet. I dared not reach for her knees to test her reflexes with the crowd watching my every move. These signs were sufficient for the time being for me to make a provisional diagnosis.

Without a word, I reached for the container of *Ganga jal* (holy water from the Ganges) and poured all of the contents onto the ground. Death was being speeded up by choking Tara with water. The old woman in the white sari stared at me with seething anger and contempt. I stood up tall, trying to look authoritative but shaking inside with unfamiliar feelings. How dare I challenge the orthodox customs?

The silence was deafening. 'What is all this? Do you all want to kill her?' I shouted. 'All of you, please go home.' There was shuffling of a few feet but nobody left. One of her nephews, the nasty one who had approached me earlier, stepped a little forward and smirked. 'Oh, she is going to live then, is she?'

'She is not dead,' I told him. 'She is unconscious. I have stopped her just in time from being choked to death. Now I will take her to the hospital, where I can treat her properly.'

'Can you guarantee that she will live?' demanded the nephew. Before I could give an appropriate answer, another nephew quietly stepped forward and asked what I thought had happened to his aunt.

'She appears to have had a burst blood vessel inside her head,' I said, trying to explain the probable diagnosis of sub-arachnoid haemorrhage as simply as possible.

Many onlookers started to drift away at this point. I had spoilt their fun. The musicians gathered their instruments. The nephews grouped together along with the family priest and began to confer among themselves. They were going to be the losers if Tara Didi survived. I started explaining the suspected diagnosis to Bharat. We were also trying to figure out the best way to transport her to the hospital. Dharan did not have an ambulance in those days. A van or truck was required to move her on a stretcher. Bharat's friend knew a Marwari businessman who rented a pick-up truck. He was about to get on his bicycle to make the arrangements when he was stopped by the nasty nephew.

'We have not seen anyone survive with a burst vein in the head,' he said. 'It is considered bad to die inside the four walls of one's own house, but it is worse and totally unacceptable for our aunt to die within the impure confines of a hospital. You cannot take her.' The finality of the statement was unmistakable. He was the principal next-of-kin.

'Treat her here, if you must,' said the polite nephew, ignoring his elder brother. Bharat was a minor and not officially adopted. He had no right to make decisions about Tara Didi. Her nephews, most of them addicted to *ganja* and gambling and totally disliked by Tara Didi, were nevertheless her next-of-kin. I had to submit to their wishes.

I made a last attempt. 'I need to put a needle into her spine to see if there is blood,' I told them. 'That procedure requires a special tool kit and a nurse to help me. Tara Didi will also need intravenous fluids for her nourishment and a special soft mattress to prevent her skin from breaking down. There are many other items to consider. How can we do all this at home? It will be very expensive and time-consuming for us to do all this here,' I persisted.

Perhaps the possibility that matters could go wrong at home and that the old lady might die after all made the nephews excited. They stood to inherit her millions, because much of her estate was ancestral property that could not be willed to Bharat. They could afford to be very generous. What a good investment and what a good way to get into the old lady's good books should she eventually survive. The conniving crooks said that they would procure everything that was needed. They would pay my fees for as many visits as necessary. I could get one of the nurses from the hospital privately to attend to her. Cost was no object for their dear aunt, they assured me.

I gave up. We transferred her to a comfortable mattress in one of the rooms downstairs and covered her with a soft quilt. I set up an intravenous drip and gave her a shot of chlorpromazine to reduce her blood pressure. Later I returned with an off-duty nurse and did a full examination. Her neck was very stiff and her fundi, the interior of her eyes, showed the classic signs of sub-arachnoid haemorrhage. A lumbar puncture confirmed the diagnosis. Her neurological status had not worsened. A few women volunteered to stay awake to report any sign of deterioration to me during the night.

I returned home later that night, partly satisfied that I had managed to intervene in time to prevent an unnatural death due to ignorance. I prayed silently to Dantakali to protect us all.

By the next morning Tara Didi had regained her alertness. There were no new signs of deterioration. I gave her a full explanation of her condition. I also told her that it was because Bharat had sent for me in time that she had not choked to death.

Strict bed rest, intramuscular injections of chlorpromazine to keep her blood pressure low, pethidine to control her headaches, and a light sloppy diet without salt were her treatment. This was the standard management of sub-arachnoid haemorrhage in those days. Tara improved rapidly. A week later I allowed her to be wheeled outside to the parlour where a huge number of visitors were waiting to see her.

She beckoned to Bharat and managed to stand whilst holding his shoulders. Overwhelmed with emotion, seeing the evident affection of her well-wishers, she was struck dumb for the first time in her life. She did *namaste* to all and stayed standing silently for a few seconds. Then she turned towards me and did *namaste* again. Holding onto Bharat, she walked slowly into the house.

CHAPTER 14

The Price of Beauty

There are some events which remain fresh in our memories and some questions which remain unanswered forever. Would Lati be alive today if I had not changed her face?

I used to see her most mornings, sweeping or doing chores at the vegetable shop just outside the small hospital in Dharan where I used to work. She was about five feet four inches tall, always covered with a dirty torn *khasto* (shawl), the original colour of which had faded long since. There would be the inevitable *beedi* (a small rolled tobacco leaf for smoking) stuck between her front upper incisors. She would hardly ever speak and when she did her voice was a whine. Her hair, glistening with lice, was matted from years of neglect. Her age was difficult to guess, but she was probably in her twenties. Her eyes were the saddest I had ever encountered. I never saw her smile or look happy. She was misery personified, exuding an aura of despair, melancholy and endurance that was difficult to describe. Would she ever find any happiness? Would she ever find a life partner?

Months passed. She looked just the same. I used to feel a terrible emotion within me, a kind of anger and frustration, a sense of my own helplessness as a doctor every time I saw her. She should have been operated on when she was a baby. This was all preventable, I thought. I wished that I were a plastic surgeon working in a good hospital where I could have treated her. Maybe then she would have some life, perhaps even get married and have a family, and escape from this servitude.

I was buying some fruit in that shop one day. I noticed her looking even more morose than usual. She was hardly aware of me standing next to her. She was silently sobbing. A lump of snot was coming out of her deformed nostril. The inevitable *beedi* was dead but still stuck between her teeth in the gap left by the cleft in her upper lip. The split middle portion of her left upper lip was crusted – she had probably bitten herself or been burnt by the *beedi*. She appeared to be totally unconcerned about her appearance. The lice were rampant in her hair.

Taking myself completely by surprise, I said to her, *'Baini, ma timilai apresan garera ali ramri pardiun?'* ('Sister, shall I try to make you a little beautiful by operating on you?') She looked at me with a pair of dull unconcerned eyes which moments later began to sparkle. With a disbelieving and challenging look, full of tears, she just nodded her head in consent. She could not speak. *'Bholi bihana aau, la?'* ('Then come to the hospital tomorrow morning?')

Walking back towards the hospital quarters where I lived, I was overwhelmed by the gravity of my own actions. What had I said? What had I committed myself to doing? I was a general medical officer, not a specialist. I was most certainly not a trained plastic surgeon, nor even a general surgeon come to that. How could I repair a cleft lip, possibly a cleft palate as well, and straighten her mouth too? What had I done? What right had I to give false hope to a woman who was already in a state of utter despair? Moreover, I had no right to make this offer of help when she had not asked for it.

It was now too late to back out. I had already committed myself. But how would I deliver what I had promised? All I could remember was assisting Dr Ram, the plastic surgeon in Victoria Hospital, Bangalore, as a junior houseman when he was correcting a cleft lip. This consultant had been trained in the USA and used to come to hospital in the longest and the most beautiful Impala convertible. We were all envious of him. I tried to remember the procedure as clearly as I could. His words of caution – infection, keloids, contractures, cavernous sinus thrombosis – began to surface from the deep recesses of my brain and my heart sank further. I had never prayed so hard before.

I went to the operating theatre of the hospital. This was mainly used as a labour room by my wife Leela, who dealt with complicated cases referred by the midwives. We were two of the three doctors in that hospital, covering a population of around one hundred thousand at the foothills of the eastern mountains. The senior medical officer was away on vacation. The hospital had very basic facilities and minimal equipment. We had to deal with all kinds of patients. I set about choosing the necessary instruments and preparing for the next day.

Lati came to the busy out-patient clinic looking as she had on the previous day. I asked one of the female orderlies to take her away and wash and shower her, particularly her head, as thoroughly as possible. The last of the out-patients left around noon. With a heavy heart, I went to the operating theatre. Lati was already transformed – she was smiling, looking clean in a hospital gown which hardly covered her fine body. Her eyes said it all. Her anticipation of the promised beauty made my heart sink further still.

Her left upper lip had not been injured; the crusting must have been dried up snot. Her cleft lip was not associated with a cleft palate. Her whining voice was part of her personality. She whined now, '*Sacchai ramri paridina ho?*' ('Are you really going to make me beautiful?')

'*Kosis garchu*,' ('I will try,') I said, putting confidence into my voice which I did not have. Her eyes spilled over with all the gratitude in the world.

I gave her 100 mg of pethidine as pre-op medication. That was all I had. I decided not to use open ether as a general anaesthetic. Nirmala, the midwife, and Bimala, an auxilliary nurse, stood on either side and held Lati's head steady. I infiltrated a local anaesthetic all around her mouth and sprayed ether to freeze the area and minimise bleeding. Ice cubes and adrenalin spray were kept handy. Ever so patiently and slowly, I began to right the wrong of nature. Would Dr Ram have been proud? She did not move a muscle throughout.

She came every day for the next few days to have the dressings changed. Slowly, the inflammation and swelling began to subside. The lip had joined. There was no keloid formation. Her mouth did not look crooked any more but she smiled continually. She would rise and do *namaste* every time I passed her shop. I used silently to thank Dantakali, the goddess who protected Dharan from her temple up on the hill.

The ever-present *beedi* disappeared and even the gap between Lati's teeth started to look attractive in a sensual sort of way. Her voice developed a musical texture. Lice were no longer visible on her carefully plaited hair. Her clothes were bright and clean. The transformation of her personality was worth all my misadventure and trepidation. More customers began to frequent that shop to vie for her attention. The shopkeeper must have noticed the increase in sales.

Weeks later I stopped at the shop to buy some mangoes. The shopkeeper attended to me himself; Lati was nowhere to be seen. When he realised that I was looking for her he opened up. 'There is no gratitude any more, Doctor *Saheb.* Lati has eloped,' he said. 'Not a word, and vanished just like that. After all that I have done for her, this is my reward,' he complained. He had found out afterwards that she had eloped with a soldier on home leave. He was angry and hurt because he had brought Lati up as his own daughter. Her parents had died while she was very young. I did not know of this background.

'I hope she never comes back. I shall never take her back again,' he continued in anger. I did not believe a word of it. Why would he not take her back? She was a valuable asset to his business. I murmured appropriate words of sympathy. Secretly, I was pleased that she had found a partner in life. I did not see her again.

Several months passed. It had been a long day for both of us. During supper that night Leela looked unusually distraught. She told me that a young woman from a nearby village had been brought in earlier that day as an emergency. She was four months pregnant. There was no sign of her partner or husband. It was too late. She was in septic shock with multiple organ failure and had died soon after. Unsuccessful backstreet abortion had killed her.

Leela looked at me intently and said softly, 'It was Lati, the girl with the cleft lip.'

CHAPTER 15

Daddy Will Make You Better

'Daddy, is Mummy dying?' asked Nandan. My five year old son had grown up bilingual. He spoke in Nepali to me but in English to his Indian mother. I looked at him a little surprised because of his choice of language. He either wanted his mother to hear our conversation or he was just frightened and had broken into English without thinking. I did not know. He came near me and held on to my leg gently. With one thumb in his mouth, he looked intently at his softly moaning mother who was lying on the bed with her eyes shut, looking pale and perspiring profusely.

'Daddy, give her an injection. That will make her better. Please, Daddy,' he said. His eyes were beseeching me. How a five-year-old could put so much pathos, entreaty and expectation into his large eyes, I shall never know. I could not speak to him. He himself had been very ill with a liver abscess a few months earlier. I had personally given him streptomycin and penicillin injections, which had cured him. He had great faith in my ability and in my injections.

This was what at last gave me the courage to inject Leela with digoxin, though I knew it could kill her. I understood that I had to give her this injection or Nandan would never forgive me for not having tried to save his mother. I broke the ampoule of intravenous digoxin and started to draw half of the liquid into the syringe.

It was January 1977. The Panchayat regime was at the height of its ruthless exploitation of Nepal. Anti-Indian slogans were considered very patriotic. All Indians were called '*Dhoti*' – an insulting and derogatory nick-name. Corruption, nepotism and favouritism were rampant. There were three Intelligence units – one run by the regular police, one military and one run from the Royal palace. The people lived in a state of constant terror, particularly outside Kathmandu, where the Police Superintendent, the Chief District Officer or the Captain of the Royal Nepalese Army could imprison, coerce or exploit anyone they liked. They could call anyone an 'anti-national element' and put him or her in jail, or make a person disappear without trace. As doctors we were protected by these thugs to a degree, as they needed us for treating their venereal diseases, conducting the deliveries of their wives and treating their children and other family members. Leela, however, being Indian, was not favoured by the establishment although she was very popular among the business community and the local youth.

We were the two medical officers in Dharan. Our small hospital was by the side of the main trail to Dhankuta. It was more like a health centre than a hospital, although we had fifteen in-patient beds and six nurses, two of whom were properly qualified. One midwife and Leela used to conduct all the deliveries in the hospital between them. They had looked after more than five thousand in the previous year. It was a very stressful job for Leela.

The King was due to visit Dharan during February, the following month. All leave had been cancelled and we had been ordered to be on our best behaviour. In addition, the week before, I had been called to the Ministry of Health in Kathmandu for extra instructions. This had come at an opportune time because I had also submitted an application for a British Council Scholarship for Tropical Community Paediatrics in Liverpool, England. I could check on the progress of my application while I was in the capital. The Ministry was to select the best candidate on the basis of their work experience, academic qualifications, published papers and annual appraisal ratings. I had been confident of getting this scholarship because nobody would be scoring higher points than me. I knew all the candidates personally.

Little did I know that the scholarship had already been awarded to someone who was related to the Health Minister. My 'exceptional' rating in annual appraisals for two years had not been taken into consideration because the Director had needed to clarify some points. Moreover, I had been penalised by ten points for disregarding orders to attend an in-service course on management. I had been fighting an epidemic at that time in the remote Himalayan villages in Karnali and had sent my letter of refusal with apologies. This letter had not been kept in my file. So not only had I lost out on the scholarship but I had been black-listed for insubordination as well. In spite of all that, I had lost out by only one point.

My hopes of going to the UK with Leela and Nandan had been cruelly dashed. This was too much for me to accept.

I made an appointment to meet the Cabinet Secretary the next day. He had come to the remote Karnali region during the epidemic and had congratulated me and Leela on our work there. I hoped to jog his memory and ask him to intervene. This man had risen rapidly from the ranks and was a favourite of the present King Birendra. He had been a middle-ranking civil servant when I was in high school and he used to come to our house to pay his respects to my father, then the Governor of Rastra Bank. However, my father had refused to buy gold utensils from the late King for the bank at a rate of $120.00 an ounce when the central banks could buy an ounce of gold in the international market for $35.00. He had subsequently been sacked by the King for this refusal. My hope was that this information was not known to the Cabinet Secretary. For whatever reason, the meeting was a disaster. He flatly refused to acknowledge the importance of my excellent appraisal record, arguing that such a rating as mine had become commonplace. His manner was very impatient and he left hastily for the Royal Palace. I had a feeling that he had indeed known of my father's plight, hence the reference to the Palace.

I had never felt so betrayed or insulted. I had worked hard. I had remained politically neutral. I had served my country and my patients well. I had already earned an international reputation in the field of community health. But it had become very clear that morning that I had no future at all in Nepal. Leela, being Indian born, could be another weakness for us and I became overtly aware of our vulnerability. I began to feel afraid for the first time. Either I had to become a personal physician to the King himself, or I had to emigrate. I made the decision to leave the country. By a stroke of good luck I managed to get a passport the next day and returned to Dharan patiently to plan our escape.

I explained all this to Leela on my return to Dharan. We budgeted, calculated the necessary travel expenses and began to correspond with the General Medical Council in England. The plan was for Leela and Nandan to follow me to England once I had got a job there. If the Nepalese government did not give Leela the necessary passport, she would have to go to India and get an Indian passport. But Leela had already taken Nepalese nationality. She could not bring herself to accept such devious methods after doing so. At the same time, she was convinced that she would not get a Nepalese passport and would be incarcerated in Nepal without me being there to fight her cause. Indeed, the King had banned all doctors, engineers, lawyers and other educated people from leaving Nepal. They would not be given a passport for at least five years from the date of application. I tried to reassure Leela, time and again, that the same man who had helped me get a passport would also help her in due course. Moreover, we had meagre savings, not the several thousands needed to finance this adventure. I had no hope of financial assistance from my father. We branched into private practice to earn as much as possible.

It was late afternoon the week after my trip to Kathmandu when a hospital orderly came to my private clinic to inform me that Leela had been taken ill. I rushed home to find that she was supporting the left side of her chest with one hand. She said that she had heart palpitations that had not stopped for an hour and she was scared. I tried to reassure her, gave her ice-cold water to sip, made her lie down on her right side and tried to make light conversation. This did not make any difference. I did not have an ECG machine in the hospital, neither was there a cardiac monitor. I examined her. There was no sign of lack of oxygen. Her pulse was about 200 beats per minute, regular and with a blood pressure of 150/80 mm Hg. I could not feel the thyroid gland in her neck; an enlarged and overactive thyroid can cause palpitations. I gently massaged her neck. Her pulse slowed a little but soon reverted to high speed. Her chest sounded clear. Her abdomen felt normal. Her legs appeared normal; there was no calf tenderness to suggest deep vein thrombosis or pulmonary embolism (blood clot within the lungs).

'It's probably a supraventricular tachycardia. This should revert back to normal spontaneously,' I said to myself and to Leela. (Supraventricular tachycardia is a very high heart rate that can be caused by stress and may right itself without any intervention.) I had some diazepam and gave her 5 milligrams to swallow. I urged her to try to sleep. She looked at me with terror-stricken eyes and whispered, 'You will look after Nandan.' I chose to understand this as a statement of no importance and told her that she should try to go to sleep without worrying about him. But I knew what she meant. She shut her eyes, clutched my hand and fell silent. A few minutes later she appeared to drift off. I gently eased my hand from her grasp and walked outside. The stress of work, fear of the unknown and impending potential dangers had proved too much for her.

There was already a small crowd outside our ground-floor flat. News that the lady doctor was ill had spread throughout the town. Two of my friends came to ask what had happened. I said she had an abnormally rapid heart beat and that some sleep would make her better. Most of the crowd went home but Shyam and Malik stayed behind, just in case I needed any assistance. Maya fed Nandan, who was asking about his mother. I explained that she was unwell and was sleeping but would get better by morning. He played with Maya for a little while and went to bed in his room. It was ten PM when a weak voice came from Leela. She needed the toilet. She was sweating profusely. Her pulse was still about 200 beats per minute but was of good volume. She collapsed on the bed upon returning from the bathroom. It had been six hours since the attack had started and she showed no improvement.

I sent Shyam to the chemist to get some propranolol. In those days this was the only beta blocker available in Dharan. I gave her 40 milligrams to swallow. She took a little drink from a glass of fresh fruit juice but she declined to eat any dinner and fell into a fitful sleep. One hour later, she was awoken by chest pains. Now I was truly worried. Unable to think of alternatives, Shyam and Malik made the decision to fetch Dr Sharma, a consultant general physician from the Koshi Zonal Hospital in Biratnagar, twenty-eight miles away. Both of them left immediately. We did not dare to take her by car to Biratnagar. There was no ambulance in those days. The treatment for heart attack was bed rest, oxygen and morphine, and prayers.

The pain was getting more severe. Five milligrams of dimorphine did not make any difference. Another 5 milligrams was given by Dr Sharma at midnight. He had brought his portable ECG machine. This showed Leela had supraventricular tachycardia with 'ischaemic changes', meaning that her heart was getting damaged due to lack of oxygen. This could have been caused by the rapid heart rate itself. By three AM her blood pressure had begun to drop and she had developed crepitations (small crackles that can be heard with a stethoscope) at the base of her lungs. She was drowsy. Whether this was due to the diamorphine or to lack of oxygen to her brain was difficult to tell. Dr Sharma would not recommend giving digoxin and we had no means of treating her with an electric shock to the heart. He said that we had done what we could and now it was in the hands of the Almighty. It was four AM. He retired to the living room to rest. His advice was to transfer her to Biratnagar Hospital at dawn.

'Oh, Lord Pashupatinath, what shall I do now?' She was sinking. If there had been sufficient light, I would have noticed the deep blue tinge over her lips and fingers. Earlier a soft moan had been coming from her. Now it was the unmistakable, rapid, laboured, breathing rattle. She clutched my hand as though saying goodbye. Do I dare give her a milligram of intravenous digoxin without a cardiac monitor, without any electrolyte monitoring and against the advice of a senior specialist? If not, do I allow her to die in front of my own eyes, stand helplessly and do nothing? What if digoxin induces cardiac arrest and she dies during the injection?

I do not know if Nandan he had had a bad dream and this had woken him up. It was most unusual for him to wake during the night. The flat was very quiet. He watched me draw the drug and held his mother's hand. He touched her face very tenderly. 'Daddy will make you better, Mummy,' he said.

I connected the ECG electrodes once again and kept lead II running, just to keep an eye on her heart rhythm. With infinite patience which I did not feel and great trepidation that I cannot describe, I began slowly to inject the drug into Leela's anti-cubital vein. It felt as though hours passed. The ECG strip ran out. Now I had no means of monitoring at all. I could only feel the thready pulse in her wrist with my left middle and ring fingers. The syringe was now empty. I pulled the hypodermic needle out and pressed the puncture site to stop any bleeding. The half milligram had made no difference. I met Nandan's eyes and told him that another dose would be necessary. It was painful for both of us to wait for fifteen minutes before I dared to give the second injection. Then we waited, Nandan silently holding his mother's hand and me with my fingers at her wrist.

The pulse in her wrist abruptly became strong and slow. She began to breathe a little more easily. The attack had subsided. Nandan was watching my face.

'Have you made her better, Daddy?' he asked.

'You've made her better, son,' I said, hugging him as I had never done before.

PART III

England

CHAPTER 16

Not A Clue

'Dr Sharp, may I start applying for jobs?' I asked.

It was during a spare moment when one patient had gone out of the consulting room and the other had decided to answer the call of nature before facing Dr Sharp. Dr Sharp did not like to be kept waiting. He was a busy man of great stature, few words and piercing eyes which did not appear to miss anything. So I seized this chance. It took a great deal of resolve on my part. Most junior doctors did not dare to address him or look him directly in the eye. But I was desperate.

Dr Sharp did not even look at me when he said, 'Present a case to me during the ward round tomorrow'. Thus dismissed, I retreated to a corner of the consulting room, trying to look as unobtrusive as before. The rest of the afternoon is a blur. I must have been preoccupied by the thought of what would follow the next day.

The night was filled with broken sleep and vivid dreams, most of which found me falling from a cliff and holding my breath, anticipating the imminent impact on the rocks below. I would wake up in a sweat, drink a glass of water and try to get back to sleep, once again to be tormented by a similar dream. I dared not take a swig of the duty-free

Chivas Regal I had bought on my journey, for fear that it might affect the sharpness of my mind when I presented the case to 'Sir' (Dr Sharp) the next day.

The General Medical Council had given me full registration. However, being a foreign medical graduate, I needed to be vetted by a senior consultant in the NHS before I could apply for jobs in the UK. Dr Sharp was the consultant assigned by the Department of Health to assess me. He would be paid extra for this work. He had been given one month to do so during which I would be doing a 'Clinical Attachment' under him. He had interviewed me on the day that I had arrived. Since then two weeks had passed but he had not spoken to me once. He held my future in his hands. There would be no appeal if he said no. Then I would have to return to Nepal.

I had been given small jobs to do by the resident house officers and registrars on call. These included clerking patients, setting up intravenous drips and taking blood samples from the patients. I had been attending all Dr Sharp's ward rounds and out-patient clinics. In addition, I used to attend the ward rounds of other medical consultants as well. My brain had become like a sponge. I had to absorb it all. I used to ask 'intelligent questions' and make my presence felt during the clinical meetings and case discussions. But Dr Sharp did not appear to have any interest in me at all. I was beginning to have serious doubts about myself.

During those two weeks I had learnt that he was the head of the department, was disliked by most of his colleagues and was referred to as 'Sir'. This was partly due to grudging envy as he was a nationally and internationally renowned authority on industrial lung diseases. He could have been a successful rugby player and stood at six foot three. His soft, clipped tones and his chin always thrust forward in a posture of aggression surely had contributed to suggest his nickname. I wondered whether he might not have acromegaly, a disorder of the pituitary gland, in which the gland produces excess growth hormone in adulthood, thickening the bones and coarsening the features. Others were not inclined to be so charitable. 'Sir' implied the imperiousness that he showed towards others; he had not been knighted.

I reached the ward office at eight am and asked the Registrar to assign a case to me so that I could present it to Sir later that morning. He knew that I was going to be assessed that day and passed a file to me. This was the briefest clerking I had ever seen, on a single page and it went something like this:

> March 30, 1977, 01:15 hrs
> Name: Su Gibson, F, act 35 years, B in F.
> Presenting complaint: O D Nitrazepam, 20 tabs, with Vodka
> History of presenting complaint: Quarrel with boy friend.
> Past medical history: Three suicidal attempts with OD
> Personal History: Cig 40; ethanol, most weekends, ?amount.
> Drugs: Nitrazepam 10 mg nocte, Amytriptilene 100 mg nocte
> Family history: Divorced, two children. Nil else
> Physical Examination: GC Good, Not drowsy. BP 120/80, pulse 85/min, reg
> Rest NAD
> Admit for observation.
> Refer Psychiatrist mane.
> Signed: not legible.

(F signifies female; OD, an overdose of drugs; NAD, no abnormality detected; Nitrazepam is a drug with calming properties; Amytriptilene is used to treat depression; and GC is short for general condition.)

I recognised the handwriting of the Registrar.

The prospect of presenting such a straightforward case alarmed me; it would not help me to impress 'Sir'. I looked in anguish at the Registrar but he ignored me and said 'Do not waste time, you have an hour.' and got on with his work. Resigned to my predicament, I went into the women's ward.

I found Su and introduced myself, pulling a chair near her. She was indifferent. I did not know how I was to break the ice in such a situation.

'Did you really mean to kill yourself?' I blurted out. She looked at me this time with the faintest of interest but did not answer. She had the eyes of a person in deep distress. There was a great sadness in her face. She was a pretty woman in spite of all her attempts to destroy herself.

'Who is looking after your children?' was my next question.

A shrug of shoulders suggesting 'I don't care' followed.

'What would have happened to them if you had died?' I asked stupidly.

That is when she broke down. She allowed me to hold her hands and I let her weep until she was able to control herself.

'Maybe I can help. Why don't you tell me?' I said gently and pulled my chair closer. She took a long hard look at me and spoke suddenly.

'Look at my tongue, doctor. Is it black?' She stuck out her tongue at me. It was pink. I said so.

Thirty minutes later I knew that she was a woman tormented by guilt and shattered self-esteem. Something could be done for her. She could be healed.

At the age of twelve, she had been sexually molested by her step-father while her mother was lying next to her in a drunken stupor. She had cursed him and her mother and wished them both dead. They had died the next day in a car crash. She had held herself responsible for the death of her mother ever since. After the foster home and rather poor performance at school, she had started as a domestic in the local hospital at the age of sixteen. She found she could not have normal relationships with boys. Any male advance triggered abhorrence and a feeling of disgust. Half-hearted attempts at suicide did not achieve anything. Finally, she had met a man who appeared to understand her and was kind. He was a long-distance driver and an orphan like herself.

They got married and had two children. It was five years later that she found out that he already had a wife and family somewhere on the south coast. She thought that she was being punished for being secretive. She had hidden the fact from him that she had been raped by her step-father. Following this separation, she began to neglect her children and social workers became involved. They took her children to safe foster homes. She took to the streets. Finally, her current boyfriend appeared sympathetic. She was now sixteen weeks pregnant. She had decided to come clean last night and had told him everything. He had become furious. There was a big quarrel. He had stormed out. She had really meant to kill herself this time. I examined her. I saw the signs of pregnancy. I could feel her womb was enlarged.

I assured her that I would try to get her help and proper social and psychiatric support. She appeared grateful. She had seen psychiatrists in the past, she said. But they had not really shown any interest and hence she had not told them everything.

I had a great case to present to Sir. I made copious notes and wrote referral slips to the social worker as well as to a consultant psychiatrist and took the file to the Registrar for his signature. He saw my clerking and the referral notes and just stared at me. His face fell. It had of course been a busy night or he would not have missed such important issues! The reality is that nobody takes half-hearted attempts at overdose seriously. These patients are considered a nuisance and a distraction by the junior medical team, who need to look after seriously ill patients. Very often, there is a cry for help in these desperate acts of OD but it usually falls on deaf ears. But I had heard Su crying from the depths of her tormented soul. I outlined her management, which included a detailed psychological evaluation, social support and rehabilitation. I was going to tell Sir about her. I was beaming with anticipation and hope.

Sir came for his ward round. Su was the penultimate patient. I took a step forward to present her. The Registrar intervened and said, 'Just another OD.' Looking at me, he continued, 'We have referred her to the psychiatrist and social services.' Sir did not even greet Su properly and with a nod moved on to the next patient. My hopes of making an impression on him were thus shattered. I felt helpless and uncertain. We moved on.

The Registrar began to present the last case.

'Mrs Windermere was admitted last night as an emergency having collapsed at home. She had been having non-specific symptoms for over six months, losing weight, feeling breathless, with vague body and joint pains and occasional bleeding from the nose…'

Sir looked concerned and asked, 'And?'

'There is nothing to find on clinical examination,' said the Registrar. 'There are several possibilities,' he blathered, crestfallen and miserable at being unable to come up with a working diagnosis. Sir asked for the case notes, looked at them and examined the chest of the patient. He beamed at her and said, 'Dr Gautam here will sort you out'. He looked at me and said, 'Come to my office after you have finished with her.'

Leaving the patient bewildered and me cursing my luck, Sir left the ward. I took a detailed history, performed a thorough examination and looked at the preliminary test results done the previous night. Mrs Windermere remained a puzzle.

'This is the end of my career in the NHS,' I thought to myself. Worse, I had been so naïve in believing in my ability that I had not bought a return ticket and neither had I sufficient money to get one now. I had left all our savings behind so that my wife and son could finance their trip to the UK. The future certainly could not have looked more grim.

I swallowed a mouthful of water. Taking a long deep breath, I threw my notes in the bin. I was not going to need them any more. Pretending to be in a cheery mood, I tried to whistle. 'Never give up and never stop; just journey on to the mountain top.' Little did Mrs Helen Steiner Rice know that I had already fallen from the mountain top!

I walked up the stairs to face my nemesis. I knocked on the door.

'Enter,' said a booming voice.

Sir was in his swivel chair, his long legs resting upon the desk, deep in conversation on the telephone. I remained standing for ages. Finally, the call was over. He looked at me and asked, 'Well?'

'Not a clue,' said I, smiling sardonically and brave as a sheep on its way to the slaughter house. He humphed, 'Hmmm.'

That said it all. I had nothing further to lose. I reached for the door-knob to get out. On an impulse, perhaps prompted by the devil in me, I asked him, 'What is wrong with her?'

'I haven't a clue,' he said.

He laughed loudly at my astonished face and said that I could start applying for jobs, beginning as a locum in his own unit to cover Easter, which was due the following week.

This was my resurrection.

CHAPTER 17

Apartheid

Leela and I were having our photograph taken at the Cape of Good Hope during a holiday in South Africa. 'Cape of Good Hope' used to conjure up all sorts of wonders in my imagination as a schoolboy. I had read that Africa was the mysterious, unexplored continent. Many had hoped to reveal its secrets and tried to reach the Cape, only to be shipwrecked and perish. I used to fantasise about being part of the crew on such a ship, navigating the Cape, braving all storms, and avoiding the almost inevitable disaster. Sometimes I would allow the shipwreck to happen and find myself floating on a timber towards Table Mountain, only to be rescued by a kindly mermaid. The legends of Table Bay and the story of the cockney lad who made millions discovering the gold mine used to be my favourite daydreams where I would substitute myself for one of the key characters.

I loved imagining the sun rising over the Indian Ocean and sinking over the Atlantic horizon. Bartholomew Dias had first named it the Cape of Storms. He can have had little premonition that this heavenly place would produce unbearable storms, not only physical but emotional and psychological, all across the world and become a symbol of man's inhumanity to man. Memories of stories connected with South

Africa began to surface from the deep recesses of my mind. From nowhere I remembered a painful incident. I must have shivered in that warm sunny day because Leela touched my hand and looked up at me. 'Are you OK?' she asked. I had never believed that South Africa would one day become a rainbow nation, able to forgive the inhumanity of man to man.

It was 1979. Nelson Mandela was on Robben Island. The Commonwealth had declared commercial sanctions against South Africa. Mrs Thatcher and Ronald Reagan continued to support the apartheid regime and the Soweto uprising had been interpreted as the evils of communism trying to take over the peninsula. Apartheid was indeed at its most brutal. I was on duty as the Senior House Officer covering emergency admissions at North Lonsdale Hospital, Barrow-in-Furness, twenty miles from Lake Windermere in England.

The Lake District is one of the most beautiful regions in England. It attracts tourists from all over the United Kingdom as well as abroad. We used to get a lot of tourists in our Accident & Emergency department.

The Senior Staff Nurse from A & E had the unmistakable sound of panic in her voice when she contacted me over the phone. She did not like the condition of the patient who had just been brought by the emergency ambulance from Lake Conniston. I rushed to A & E.

One nurse had just finished doing an ECG and the other was recording the patient's blood pressure. The huge figure of a Caucasian man was lying on the trolley. An oxygen mask was over his face. His eyes were shut. He was softly grunting and clutching at his chest. Jill, the coronary care nurse, handed me the ECG strip. It showed a massive heart attack. Immediate action was indeed essential. I attempted to feel his pulse, saying at the same time, 'Mr Reebock, I am Dr Gautam. May I examine you?'

The eyes opened with enough venom to annihilate the world. 'Don't touch me,' he hissed, with the ferociousness of a cobra. 'Call your superior,' he ordered.

Taken aback at this sudden and unexpected reaction to my polite attempts at ministration, I recoiled in horror. The three nurses turned pale at first, becoming red-faced when the reason for this outburst dawned on them. Jill pointed at the admission papers. I read: Januck Reebock, aged forty-eight years. Home address: The Serpentine, Cecil Road, Cape Town, South Africa. Current Address: Hotel Windermere, Windermere, Cumbria.

I had heard of apartheid but had never experienced it. Clearly the man was seriously ill and needed urgent help. This was not the time to feel offended. For all I knew, he might already be suffering from cerebral hypoxia and hence have impaired judgement.

'You are in great pain and very ill. Let me first give you some diamorphine and set up an intravenous drip. I shall then call my senior doctor as you wish,' I said with all the courage of a trembling mouse. The venomous eyes opened in anguish. Once again he hissed, 'Don't you dare do anything. Call your superior.'

Truly dumbfounded, I recoiled and went into the office cubicle. I picked up a phone and called John Eagles, my Registrar. He was a Caucasian and an Englishman. He would not have been able to see my shaking hands but my staccato speech was difficult to hide.

'Speak up man. What are you mumbling about?' John asked. Ashamed of my own weakness, I tried to compose myself.

'There is this massive anterior infarction from South Africa who won't allow me to touch him and wants to see you,' I said. There was silence for a few seconds until John had assimilated the content of my shaky speech.

'Are you calling me because you have difficulty in treating him?' he asked.

'No, I can manage him alright if he would let me, but he insists on seeing you.'

'Tell him that you have spoken with me and that I have sufficient confidence in you to treat him. I am not coming.' He disconnected the phone.

I had not seen any meanness in John's behaviour towards me or anyone else during the nine months that I had known and worked with him. He had a very strong sense of moral outrage over how the British had colonised the world. Obviously a man of great social conscience, John must have inherited this sense of fair play from his father. Rumour had it that although a promising neurologist, the senior Dr

Eagles had not been able to conform to the close-knit establishment of the National Neurological Hospital in London and returned to the Lakes to become a general practitioner. I had a feeling that John too would not budge from his convictions.

'Mr Reebock. I have spoken to my Registrar, Dr Eagles. He has asked me to tell you that he has full confidence in me to look after you. He is not coming. You are very ill. Please let me give you this injection.'

'Over my dead body! Get lost. Tell him to come now or else I will go.' The threat was unmistakable. I retreated back to the phone.

I told John what had happened, knowing full well that he would not come. But the patient desperately needed help. I could not just let him die. I felt that his personal views about the human race were irrelevant at this moment of crisis.

'Let me make it clear. Are you or are you not capable of treating him?' John asked.

'Of course I can treat him, if he would only let me,' I said sadly.

'Tell him I am not coming. This is a free country; if he wants to walk away, let him.'

'John, this is not the time. Please come if you can,' I entreated again.

'I am busy. I will see him on my rounds later.' The line went dead.

'Mr Reebock, Dr Eagles is busy. He will see you during his rounds later. Let me treat you,' I begged again.

'You f***ing coloured ass. Get me out of here.'

He tore off the oxygen mask and pulled off the wires of the heart monitor. He swung himself off the trolley and stood up. The sight of a tall, plethoric, obese man mouthing obscenities made us all cringe. Jill shielded me and held my hand. The other nurse gave him his shirt and jacket. He staggered out of the cubicle and on into the corridor, towards the main door.

None of us was able to speak. We stood, looking at each other in disbelief. Jill, always the resourceful staff nurse, went to boil the kettle for a revitalising cup of tea.

A few moments later there was a loud crash call of cardiac arrest. Abandoning the tea we ran towards the door and outside where we found a man had collapsed on the driveway. He was dead. It was Mr Reebock.

CHAPTER 18

It Works Both Ways

It was a horrible nightmare. I was being chased by a horde of demented and naked old men and women along the corridors of the Royal Liverpool Hospital. I wanted them to stop but they kept on coming towards me. They were brandishing walking sticks, zimmers and tripods which were raised for a lethal strike. Catheters and leg bags were being dragged. I was running away from them as fast as I could. There was no place to hide. I tried to open doors but they were locked fast. I was exhausted. I fell and curled up, protecting my face. A confusing cacophony of shouts was deafening my ears. I awoke with a start, my throat was dry, my heart was pounding and my body was wet with perspiration. The alarm was ringing. It was seven AM. I arose with great trepidation to begin my day. I began to get ready for my first day as a Locum Registrar in Geriatric Medicine at the Royal Liverpool Hospital.

I had resigned the previous week as a Registrar in radiology after completing one year of training. In essence this meant that I had thrown away a potentially very lucrative career. It was a highly technical field involving huge machines, lots of physics and darkness. I hated to work in darkness. I missed clinical work and patient contact.

I had been a clinician for twelve years and I longed for interaction with patients. But I had never bargained for a career in geriatric medicine. I had no experience of it and had vague misconceptions about this specialty. The thought of spending the rest of my professional career looking after the old, demented, incontinent and bedridden was not at all to my liking. Surely there was a better way to earn a living?

The postgraduate Dean had sounded very positive when I had gone to seek his advice. He had said that the specialty needed people like me. I was not sure whether he was just patronising me. He had been apologetic when he told me that I did not appear to have any chance of progression in cardiology in the UK. I knew that for myself, of course. I had worked in that specialty for nearly three years, written papers and conducted research. I was told repeatedly how good I was at my work. But somebody else had been appointed as Senior Registrar; I was not even invited for an interview. This setback had prompted me to try radiology, which I did not like. The Dean then asked me to go to see the Professor of Geriatric Medicine. The Professor was a man of few words. He had skimmed through my curriculum vitae, peered at me and asked, 'Are you sure you want to do geriatrics?' I had told him that I was not sure. He paused, and then told me to try it out. He had offered me the locum job in his firm for two months. I was to start the next day. That was the origin of my nightmare.

I started at eight AM. It was October 1984. I attended the unit review meeting, followed by a talk on the longevity of Amazonian people from a fifth-year medical student. He had recently returned from there after a six-week elective period of study. I was then asked to conduct the outpatient clinic. There were four new and ten repeat consultations. I forgot that I had done no clinical work for over a year. I managed without any difficulty. No one had dementia or incontinence. The four new patients had complicated medical histories which were further complicated by new symptoms and needed sorting out. I liked those kinds of challenges. My last patient had come for a six-monthly review. I read his notes and became curious. It did not feel right somehow.

Mr Cox was seventy-two years old. Six years before he had been told that he had developed Parkinson's disease. He had retired aged sixty-five from his job as a manager in a large multinational company. Before he could emigrate to Florida to spend his money on an expensive yacht, bungalow and a new lifestyle, his coronary arteries had caught up with him. He had been lucky to survive a massive heart attack during his retirement party. His heart had gone into complete block, which required a pacemaker to keep it ticking. He had recovered very well, minus the confidence to start a new life in Florida. He kept a small boat at Southport, continued to live in Blundellsands, and was picking up the threads of his life when his hypertensive wife died unexpectedly from a massive stroke. It was difficult to get over the bereavement. Mr Cox began to spend more time on his yacht. Then he began to feel dizzy, particularly when he was adjusting the sails, climbing up the mast and painting the boat. He had almost fainted several times.

His GP prescribed him Stemetil (betahistine). His cardiac pacemaker was reported to be working fine. But Mr Cox did not get better. His days at the boat became more and more difficult. He blacked out a couple of times, yet no cause for this was found. A CT scan of his brain was reported as normal. He began to be depressed and lost his bearings a few times. He was then started on thioridazine and amitriptyline. He began to slow down considerably and regretfully sold the yacht. He was subsequently seen by someone in our department and diagnosed with Parkinson's disease. He was given Madopar, which helped a little but the disease continued to get worse. His GP had not entertained his request to seek a second opinion. He was not a happy man when I saw him that morning.

The history appeared to suggest that the dizziness was the forerunner of his slow deterioration. He had recovered well from his heart attack. The pacemaker was checked and was reported to be functioning normally. It had been replaced the previous year with the same brand, a device that would pace the heart if it did not detect any heart beat. On the other hand, if it detected a heart beat above sixty beats per minute, it would not pace the heart (VVI). I examined him thoroughly. His voice was a whisper, and his movements were laboured and tremulous. His arm was very stiff when we shook hands. I checked his blood pressure lying down and standing up. There was a significant drop in systolic pressure when he stood up but he did not become dizzy. He did show signs of advanced Parkinson's disease. I could not figure out the cause of his original dizziness. I decided to use a portable electrocardiogram to assess his heart. It was pacing at seventy beats per minute. All the pacing blips appeared normal. On an impulse, I asked him to do a manoeuvre. Bingo. I discovered the cause of his dizziness. He did not have Parkinson's disease; he had been the subject of medical ignorance and the side effects of horrible drugs for the past six years.

I had asked him to stand and press on the wall with both hands as hard as possible. The ECG machine was kept on, churning the tracing of Lead II, which shows the rhythm of the heart. Suddenly these steady paced beats stopped and a set of fast oscillations began to appear. 'I am feeling dizzy,' he whispered and promptly became limp. I was anticipating this and the Staff Nurse who was helping me was also ready to assist in just such an eventuality. We prevented him from falling down and put him on the couch. He surfaced instantly and looked at me, uncomprehending.

I assured him that he was OK. I explained that the diagnosis was a 'myopotential inhibition of a pacemaker'. In simple words, the pacemaker would sense the contraction of his pectoral muscles and stop pacing whenever that happened. As a result his heart would stop beating and he would feel dizzy. He would faint if this continued for a while. I explained that his pectoral muscles would have been contracting when he climbed to reach the top of the mast or was changing the sails or painting his boat. I assured him that we would be able to fix the problem. His pacemaker needed to be reprogrammed to a continuously pacing mode. It could be done within a few minutes. I would be arranging this. I advised him to expect a letter from the Cardiologist at Broadgreen Hospital in the very near future.

I also advised him to come off Stemetil and thioridazine. These drugs had side effects mimicking Parkinson's disease and were probably responsible for his condition. He would take some time to recover and hence he should continue with the Madopar and amitriptyline for a little longer but start reducing their dosages. I gave him a routine appointment for follow-up in six months. 'You should be ready for discharge from our department by then,' I said.

Mr Cox was delighted and very impressed. Apparently, according to him, no-one had given him such a thorough examination before.

I had subjected Mr Cox to a crude and perhaps risky manoeuvre. It was not proper to attempt this in an out-patient clinic without full resuscitation facilities. But I was excited by the thought that there was this possibility and wanted to check it out for myself. 'Nobody else would think to look for myopotential inhibition in an advanced Parkinsonian like him,' I justified to myself. I had been carried away by the thought that this poor man's dreams had been destroyed by medical ignorance and inappropriate prescribing.

The truth was that Mr Cox had jogged my memory. I had remembered an unusual case which I had encountered a couple of years earlier. I was then being trained as a Registrar in Cardiology at Broadgreen Hospital in Liverpool. I used to insert about four pacemakers each week and was developing a special interest in cardiac electrophysiology. I had put in a pacemaker for a fifty-year-old patient from the Isle of Man. It was a VVI pacemaker for complete heart block. It was an uneventful procedure and he had returned to the Isle of Man. He was well at first but began to faint whenever he tried to hug his wife. He was most embarrassed when he had blacked out just before reaching the climax of their most intimate moment. He had been sent back to us by the local GP to see if the pacemaker was functioning correctly. We had investigated him thoroughly and found nothing wrong. But clearly, something was awry.

In those days we were aware of a host of unexplained symptoms which were grouped together as 'pacemaker syndrome'. I had then conducted a thorough search of the scientific literature for this syndrome and come across a few similar case reports. These had turned out to be cases of myopotential inhibition of pacemakers. This was new to most of us in the department. The condition was confirmed in our patient when I checked again. We had reprogrammed his pacemaker to a continuously pacing mode. His symptoms had disappeared and he had been able to hug his wife and make up for lost time. (As my luck would have it, another doctor wrote a leading article based on that case and did not even have the courtesy to acknowledge my contribution. Such were the times for overseas doctors in specialties like cardiology; they were very exclusive.) Our knowledge of cardiac electrophysiology has progressed a great deal since then.

I wrote a referral letter to my former boss in the cardiology department, including the ECG tracing, and suggested that perhaps the patient's pacemaker could be reprogrammed to a continuously pacing mode. This was done within a few days of my referral without any further investigations. My former boss had obviously not forgotten me. I did not see Mr Cox again during my time as a locum.

A letter arrived from Mr Cox about six months later. It had been forwarded from the hospital to my home address, as I no longer worked there. He had been discharged by the Professor, whom he had told how disappointed he was to know that I had left his firm. He was keen to tell me personally that he felt a new man. He was well. He was not taking Madopar or any other drug any more. He had wanted to buy a yacht but his new lady friend was not very fond of sailing. Instead, they were exploring the possibility of moving to Spain. He was most grateful for what I had done for him.

Little did he know that it was the other way round. It was he who had given me the great confidence boost I needed in my new career. He had made me realise the value of practising holistic medicine and the challenges this offered to the intelligence of an internist. As a patient, he was an example of what the arrogance and ignorance of doctors can produce. As a healthy human being, he showed what their knowledge and dedication could achieve. He taught me what geriatric medicine was all about.

CHAPTER 19

What A Smell

It is strange how events that occur in one's formative years can continue to exert their influence all through one's life.

I was laughed at by my lecturer for a project I had done on urine during my pathology studies at medical school. I had started my report with the physical appearance in terms of colour, consistency and quantity, which could give a clue to the underlying illness. Then I had moved on to the smell of urine, at which point he had dryly asked me why I had left out its taste. The group attending this tutorial had been hugely amused and I had become an object of ridicule. (Now I am convinced that most of us became good doctors in spite of those ignorant teachers.) To my surprise, two years later in our final examination, one of the essays we had to write was on the significance of urine examination in clinical practice. Suicidal it might have been, considering the remarks made by the lecturer, but I decided to write the same project work with extra emphasis on odour. I secured the highest marks on this paper. Perhaps this experience is the reason why I am always conscious of smells emanating from patients when trying to think of the possible diagnoses.

I thought nothing of the bad smell when I was running to attend to a cardiac arrest call in a Sunderland hospital one midnight in January 1987. I had rushed out of bed forgetting to put in my lower front teeth. My dentist was making me a new bridge and had given me this temporary plastic denture for a couple of days. I ran the short distance to the next building and slipped on the frozen snow outside the front door of the ward. Witnessed by two young nurses going for their break, I bruised my coccyx and my pride rather badly. What a giggle I provoked. Picking up my pride and pretending that it was nothing, I took two steps at a time, entered the ward, ran half way across and went up the stairs to one of the private rooms where the cardiac arrest had occurred. It was while I was bounding up the stairs that I became aware of an awful smell.

I recognised the heart-attack patient. I had admitted him with a deep femoral vein thrombosis indicated by a swollen lower leg two days earlier. He was an executive in the local shipyard. This was due for closure soon and he was looking forward to the forced retirement next month. The two doctors on duty were both trying to resuscitate him. They had tried the standard treatment with no response. They needed guidance for more specialised management. Hence I was called as I was the Senior Registrar and lived within the hospital premises, even though I was not on call that night. It looked like a massive pulmonary embolism. We struggled with him for the next two hours, treating him as best we could. He came round and showed some improvement, but rapidly deteriorated once again and did not respond to the treatment. I pronounced him dead at two AM.

A successful resuscitation gives a thrill which makes one forget all the running, breathlessness, falling, or the lack of sleep. The surge of adrenalin continues in both the patient and the doctor. But when it is unsuccessful, we all try to pretend that we have not been affected. We assume a phoney professional façade and strut away, if lucky, to a quiet corner to try to gather ourselves back together. Unfortunately, the most senior doctor in the team has to face the relatives of the dead and break the bad news. Then the detailed medical notes must be written before allowing an escape to brief solitude. Formalities duly completed, I walked down the stairs, immersed in my own thoughts as to whether I could have done anything else for that patient. Half way down the stairs I became aware of the smell again.

I stopped. It was three AM. I looked around the women's ward. It was dimly lit; all the patients appeared to be sleeping peacefully. The two nurses were sitting at the far end with mugs of cocoa and knitting for company. It all looked very normal. I sniffed again. The smell was emanating from a bed very close to the staircase.

I approached the nurses' station and softly asked about the patient on that bed. One of the nurses informed me that she was a new patient admitted that night and had not yet been clerked. Both the young doctors were upstairs and had been busy. The house officer would be coming to see her presently. When admitted, her pulse and blood pressure had been fine and she had had a mild temperature. She was under four-hourly observations and was due for a check-up in fifteen minutes. Neither of these nurses was fully State Registered. I asked for the Staff Nurse in charge and was told that she was a part of the cardiac arrest team and had gone upstairs to attend to a case. I informed them that there was a horrible smell coming from that bed. One of them went to investigate. She pulled the curtains and lifted the quilt. She came back to inform me that the patient was deeply asleep and had become faecally incontinent. She then rushed back with the other nurse to clean the patient up.

I began to leaf through the incomplete admission file lying on the table. The patient was a woman aged twenty years, married with two small children. She had felt vaguely ill since lunchtime. She had vomited once, developed a faint rash over her left chest, and felt feverish. She had tried to think of it as a mild viral infection and taken a paracetamol tablet. When her husband had returned from work in the evening and found her looking unwell, he had insisted that she come for a check-up. The casualty card said that the doctor had seen her at ten thirty-five PM. He had cursorily examined her and had queried a viral illness but as an afterthought, had decided to admit her overnight for observation. He had taken a sample of blood for routine examination and cultures. According to the nursing notes, at ten fifty-five PM she had looked well, had walked into the ward carrying one child and was accompanied by her husband and her other son. The husband had taken the children home once she was settled. The cardiac arrest call had gone soon after that and the senior nurse from the ward had gone upstairs to attend to that emergency.

The nurses were behind the curtains. It felt rather odd to me that a mother of two could be so fast asleep as to become faecally incontinent. I parted the curtains and went to see the patient. They had stripped her and were in the process of cleaning her up. The patient was not protesting. The nurses were reprimanding her for becoming so irresponsible as to do it in her bed. How could she? She did not reply.

The smell was horrendous, and the nurses weakly protested by saying to me, 'Doctor, she is not ready yet, give us a few minutes.' I was already alarmed by the scene. I had smelt the incontinence while running up the stairs three hours earlier and nothing had been done about it. Valuable time had already been lost; immediate action was indeed necessary. I reached for the bed light, completely disregarding the nurses' protestations. The woman was unconscious. She was cold and several bluish blotches were well accentuated on the pale pink skin of her body. Her fingers and toes were turning dark blue. I tried to flex her neck and it felt stiff. I lifted one leg and bent it over her abdomen. The classic 'Kernig's sign' was positive. She had acute blood poisoning from a meningococcal infection.

The nurses were positively glaring at me for daring to examine a semi-naked young woman in this unconventional way, while she was lying in a pool of faeces, and I was un-gloved and showing no sense of decorum. I covered her dirty body with a clean white sheet whilst hissing at them that she was dying of meningitis. She needed penicillin, fast. More nurses miraculously appeared and began to help. They wiped her as clean as possible very quickly. Within minutes, we had given her a hefty dose of penicillin and chloramphenicol, set up an intravenous saline drip, performed a lumbar puncture, got the blood results from the lab and confirmed the toxic state due to a severe infection. The final confirmation of meningococcal infection would follow within the hour. She was in shock already and needed intensive care. We transferred her to a trolley to push her to the intensive care unit where I changed into hospital greens, discarding my soiled clothes. I did all that was necessary and then returned to my room.

It was well after six AM by now but still dark. I became acutely aware of my aching buttock. Could I have broken my coccyx? A stretch on the bed was quite a temptation. The night had been most eventful, to say the least. One patient had died. Would the other survive? Who would look after her children if she did not? Going back to bed for a little snooze was now unattractive. I decided to get ready for the day ahead. I wished to see her before I started my routine work. I headed towards the shower, glancing in the mirror on the way. Then I saw. I knew why all the people I had come in contact with that night had smiled at me politely whilst hiding their grins. The face in the mirror was that of a haggard young man without his four bottom front teeth. I laughed out loud at the image in the mirror.

The young lady survived, minus a few toes and the tip of her right middle finger. I presented this case in our grand rounds. I claimed that it was the investigation of the smell that had alerted me to the diagnosis. If it had not been for the odour, I would not have interfered and the delay of a further few hours might have proved fatal. At the end of the presentation, amidst applause, which were highly unusual, the Senior Consultant credited my nose with saving the patient.

CHAPTER 20

Back Home

It felt very good. I was excited. I looked out of the window at a clear sunny day in September 1999. I could make out Blackpool in the distance and the peaks of Snowdonia on the horizon. The view reminded me of a time long ago. Good to be home, I thought, and turned my attention to the pile of papers on my desk. I was beginning my new job as a Consultant Physician with special interest in Geriatric Medicine in Barrow-in-Furness.

But I could not concentrate and kept drifting off into the past. I had first come here, to the North Lonsdale Hospital, on 15 March 1977, my birthday according to the Nepali calendar. I had turned thirty-two years old that day and was ready to start my professional life in the National Health Service. I had come to see a senior physician in that hospital for a clinical assessment – that is, to be tested to see whether I was competent enough to practise as a junior doctor in the UK. After a month, I was given the green light. Barrow became my home for the next four years, working and studying for the higher professional examinations. In the years since, I had remained in touch with some local friends. I was indebted to the people of Barrow, who had been kind to us in the early days, and to the institution that had taught me so much.

One of my former consultants had become the head of the Department of Medicine. He understood that I was contemplating a change, perhaps a sabbatical leave, from my current job. He agreed to look into the possibility of my coming back to Barrow. The hospital had not been able to fill the vacant position of consultant geriatrician for over a year. I felt greatly privileged and humbled to be asked to take it. How many foreign medical graduates get a chance to go back to their first institution to serve as senior consultants? I swiftly resigned as a consultant and senior lecturer in Aberdeen, one of the most prestigious jobs in my specialty in the country, and committed myself to a new start in Barrow. (Leela and the children remained in Aberdeen from where I was to become a weekly commuter.)

'Do not be a sentimental fool. Get on with your work,' I said to myself.

I began to concentrate on the job in hand. Among the papers was a brief request from a GP for a domiciliary assessment visit to an old lady in a nursing home near one of the lakes. She had been deteriorating in a non-specific way for no apparent reason. I decided to call on her that very afternoon. Felicity, my new secretary, produced the relevant medical records, a stack approximately two inches thick.

It was nearly lunchtime before I had completed all the correspondence and other formalities associated with my new appointment. I began to munch on a sandwich and go through the medical records. The covers were in tatters. The last entry was two years old. I read through the correspondence, inspected the results of various investigations, and finally reviewed the reports from the social worker, physiotherapists and the occupational therapist. I had a fairly good idea of the sequence of events that had led to this lady being admitted to a nursing home; it appeared very straightforward. She was a widow, aged seventy-four, without any children, who had been admitted with a sacral pressure sore, double incontinence, depression and immobility. I had no idea when I set off in my car that afternoon what I would find twenty minutes later.

The Matron of the nursing home was expecting me. She had informed the patient, who had apparently shown complete indifference at the news.

'She is not bothered what we do or who comes to see her, not that she has many visitors, mind,' she said. I was taken to the room, which was dark and full of the familiar stench: the standard and liberal dose of air freshener mixed with the putrid aroma of gangrenous ulcer, decomposed urine and body odour. The window was firmly closed. Sunshine is not normally available in plenty in Barrow and heating is expensive.

'The consultant is here to see you, Nellie,' Matron shouted at the heap of duvet on the single bed.

A tangle of long white hair obscured the face before me. Matron scraped the hair into a ponytail, and then reached to open the window at my request. A burst of fresh air and some natural light entered the room. I could breathe more easily. The patient had undone her hair again by now and was staring at me through the strands with the utmost indifference. There was something vaguely familiar about that head of hair. I took her hand and said, 'I am Dr Gautam, Mrs Bishop.' She made no attempt to grasp my hand in return. She remained limp and lifeless. There was no acknowledgement of my introduction. She shut her eyes. Then it hit me… 'Driving School, Rawlinson Street,' I declared.

A few seconds later her eyes opened and peered at me with curiosity. I had connected right, I was now sure. Mrs Nellie Bishop had loved her silky platinum curls; she had been a stylish lady, smoking long thin cheroots in a gold and silver cigarette holder. She had run her husband's business in Rawlinson Street. They had had a huge white bloodhound that would growl at me on entering the office. Mr Jack Bishop had taught me to drive, with all the patience and encouragement of a saint. We had subsequently become friends and Nellie would often join us at the Harbour, the pub next door to the hospital, where Jack and I liked to set the world to rights on my evenings off duty.

'How is Jack?' I asked. He had been nearing sixty when I had last seen him. Her eyes softened but she had not yet recognised me. There was no answer. Clearly, I would be with her for some time. Matron was looking puzzled; she had evidently never met Jack and did not know of my Barrow connection. I thanked her and assured her that I would be able to manage alone for the time being. I would, however, need some assistance examining Mrs Bishop a little later. She left us reluctantly. She was going to miss an opportunity to pick up some juicy gossip from the past, she was sure.

'It must be twenty-odd years since I last saw you,' I said. 'You baby-sat for us a few times. My son used to play with your dog when Jack took me driving.' I supplied further pieces of the story to revive her memory. As the cobwebs parted she grabbed my hand and began to sob. It took some time for her to control herself.

'Jack died fifteen years ago. You were not there to save him this time.' Then I remembered. He had suffered a mild heart attack just before I left Barrow. I had treated him in the Coronary Care Unit. He had not stopped chain-smoking even after that scare.

Our memories thus reunited, we talked for a long time. I was in no hurry. Nellie had sold the driving school after Jack had died. She had become active in her church. The beloved dog had died two years later. Her health had been fine, except for her spine. She had begun to drag her right leg a few years later and had had to go to the neurosurgical centre in Preston for an operation. She had then required a second operation to prevent paralysis of both legs. That had been ten years ago. The second operation had been successful but it had left her with poor control of her bowel. This could occasionally be embarrassing but she had coped; she had been able to walk and to continue her work for the church. This had been until five years ago when she had fallen at the altar while attempting to reach the pulpit to polish the wood.

Her left hip had been broken during this fall. After the operation to repair it she had developed a sacral pressure sore, which had got worse. She had been unwell ever since. Her spine had begun to hurt again and she had been treated with powerful anti-inflammatory drugs. Her legs had begun to swell up. She had also developed bloody diarrhoea. She could not go home.

A camera test of her bowels had raised the possibility of cancer. This had happily been disproved at operation. Sadly though, a piece of gauze had been left behind when her stomach was sewn back up. She had suffered from stomach pains for six months until they had operated again and found it. The wound had subsequently taken a long time to heal. She had been given a catheter, yet had suffered from frequent urine infections. She had then been told that her kidneys had been affected. She could no longer walk and had become very weak. She was not interested in food or drink. She just wanted to join Jack. Life had nothing left to offer.

I listened intently to this history. Nellie's medical notes did not say that most of her problems had been created for her by her doctors, however well-meaning. But reading between the lines, the sequence of events had probably gone something like this:

First, a lumbar disc had prolapsed. The operation to correct it had led to complications, including a possible blood clot. The second operation had been to get rid of the clot. During this procedure her sacral nerves had been damaged leading to faecal incontinence.

Then, following her fall, the resultant fracture of the neck of her femur (the long bone in her thigh) had been repaired by a surgeon known for his incompetence during my early years in that hospital. Mrs Bishop had not subsequently been mobilised soon enough and had developed a sacral pressure sore from lying in bed too long. There was no evidence that proper rehabilitation had been provided. She began to limp.

When she had started to suffer from back pain again it had been treated with powerful non-steroidal anti-inflammatory drugs. These had probably caused colitis, an inflammation of her large bowel causing bloody diarrhoea, and raised CEA. This is a chemical in the blood that rises in diseases of the bowel, including cancer. A possible cause had been investigated via a poorly conducted colonoscopy. The biopsy report was non-specific and non-committal – in other words, completely unhelpful.

Ater further assessments in three different hospitals, a laparotomy had then been done in Manchester to explore these symptoms; nothing had been found. A piece of gauze had been left behind. Her condition had continued to deteriorate over the next few months. Subsequently, the second operation, done in Barrow, to rectify this error had been followed by problems with wound healing.

Rather than her drug regime being reviewed she had been prescribed yet more drugs – what is called 'polypharmacy'. These caused yet more side-effects including fluid and salt retention leading to high blood pressure. Not surprisingly, she had become depressed.

The drugs she was taking had started to cause urinary retention and associated incontinence. Being catheterised to deal with this problem had led to recurrent infections and these, along with dehydration and the non-steroidal anti-inflammatory drugs, had caused chronic renal failure.

Poor assessment of her condition had then led to inappropriate placement in the nursing home. Her life's savings had been used up. Finally, she had been forced to sell her house to finance this cruel and inappropriate move into long-term care.

'My heart was broken when I was forced to sell the house to pay for the nursing home,' she revealed, looking around with total disgust. 'Jack bought that house for me with all his severance pay when he came out of the Navy. We even spent our honeymoon there,' she reminisced.

Matron delegated Nellie's examination to the lowliest nurse in the establishment. She had not liked being dismissed earlier. She made her point rather well, I thought.

I noted Nellie's emaciated body due to malnutrition, her atrophied lower limbs due to lack of use and a four by three inch pressure sore with two smaller satellite lesions on her lower back. She agreed to be admitted to the hospital under my care. Matron was delighted that her difficult patient would be gone for a long while, thus freeing up considerable nursing time.

I asked to see all of Nellie's medications. She had been prescribed four kinds of analgesics including opiates; two antidepressants; a long-term antibiotic; two anti-hypertensives; two sleeping pills; one proton pump inhibitor; two antacids; and two laxatives. She had been taking sixteen different drugs every day in varying dosages and frequencies.

Nellie really needed calories and extra nutrients. Our nurses and the hospital nutritionist did a great job. She became stronger and the pressure sores began to heal a little. Eventually, it became apparent that she required a skin graft. It took three months before she could stand independently. As suspected, her hip had been fixed badly causing a two-inch shortening of her left leg. A shoe raise helped considerably. Regular toileting managed to control her faecal incontinence.

Self-catheterisation of the bladder controlled her urinary incontinence and over-flow problems. Gradual weaning off the opiates cured her constipation. Sleeping pills were replaced by short-acting chloral. Satisfied with progress thus far, I transferred Nellie to a cottage hospital for further rehabilitation. She responded well to simple paracetamol as required and a small dose of chloral for the night. She was a changed woman and was keen to move into independent sheltered accommodation.

I discharged her from regular follow-up after six months of continued improvement. By this time she could walk well, with a stylish walking stick. She had left the nursing home for sheltered accommodation and had started to volunteer in church once again. I presented her case at one of our departmental clinical meetings, which did not go well!

I had been unable to convince the social worker to help Nellie buy back the old house in Rawlinson Street. I would have readily supported her claim for compensation, no doubt with Jack's hearty approval. But Nellie was unwilling to pursue any claims; her case was complicated and could have dragged on for years. She preferred to forget the whole painful experience and was ultimately delighted to be enjoying life once again. Though she was not back in her old house, she felt she was back where she belonged – as did I.

PART IV

Scotland

CHAPTER 21

A Rainy Day

He lived in a cold house in an upmarket area of the city. He was a frail old man, considered a difficult patient by his GP. His social worker thought him rather weird; 'eccentric' was the word she used. He would not allow anyone to enter his house. Prompted by the social worker, the GP had made an unwelcome house call.

'I shall ask for you when I need you,' he had told the visiting GP, clearly irritated by the unsolicited intrusion. 'I feel fine, thank you very much,' he had added whilst bolting the front door. The GP had been concerned at his patient's emaciated state and unsteadiness, and had requested that I perform a domiciliary assessment.

It was a grey, *dreich* November day, with a cold northerly wind and drizzling rain. Thankfully, I did not have far to travel. Number 22 was easy to spot. An ornate Victorian wrought-iron gate opened onto a short driveway. There was no answer to my ring on the doorbell. There was no light visible in any of the rooms. I walked to the rear of the house, where the side gate was unlocked. I entered the spacious, overgrown garden. I crossed to the back door, which was also locked. I knocked repeatedly. There was no answer. Retreating a little, I looked at the upstairs windows. I thought I had glimpsed a slight movement of the curtain over one of these. Was it my imagination? I returned to the front and tried the doorbell again. Still no response. I became convinced that the patient was inside but was not amenable to being visited.

The large house was traditional, detached, and boasted six chimneys. According to my dear friend David, who knows about these things, this meant that the owner was possibly six times richer than most people with just one chimney. I needed to get into the house in order to assess the old man. I needed help but doubted whether any neighbour would come out to talk to me on such a *dreich* day.

I walked to the end of the avenue where there was a corner shop. The shop was warm and well lit. A bored assistant was leafing through a magazine, trying not to nod off. There was no one else in sight. I think she was glad of the interruption. I brought out my best smile and informed her that I was not a customer. She became quite inquisitive and chatty when I introduced myself as a consultant from the hospital. She said that she had seen my patient, Mr McBain, about a week ago. He had bought some porridge oats and a bag of potatoes. She knew that he was a wealthy solicitor, widowed for six years. She described him as a miserly old man and told me of his refusal to donate to the church jumble sale. She had not forgotten how he had slammed the door on her last year. He was definitely not known to be the life and soul of a party. What a shame it was that the kindly Mrs McBain had died so unexpectedly after a short illness. She had always had time for friends and neighbours. Despite this interesting information, when I turned to leave I was still unsure of how to access the house.

In walked the local minister just at that moment. Apparently, he was a regular customer in that shop for its special Aberdeen Butterye, a firm deliciously thick pancake-like preparation, containing thousands of calories. We were introduced by the assistant. He too had no idea of how to approach the man. Mr McBain had stopped attending the kirk after the death of his wife. In a sudden flash of inspiration, I asked the minister to accompany me to Number 22.

We repeatedly rang the bell but, as expected, there was no response. I knocked at the door quite loudly, shouting that I was the doctor from the hospital and that I had the minister with me as a witness. I called out as loudly as possible and threatened to call the police and ambulance to break the door down if he did not let us in. After repeating these threats a few times, we waited for a while in silence.

This was a liberty I was not authorised to take. I did not like myself for threatening and frightening an old man but I could not think of any other way of getting to see him. There was definitely the prospect of finding a dead body in a few days time, or a body on the floor in a state of fatal hypothermia. Such scenarios could be prevented by timely intervention. The minister, however, was clearly uncomfortable with my unorthodox approach. He tried to hide his embarrassment behind his bag of shopping. I explained apologetically that I felt my actions were justified in the interests of the patient. His expression nevertheless betrayed his difficulty in understanding the situation. He shuffled his feet in silence. Then, we heard some movement inside and the door opened.

An old man in a tatty woollen dressing-gown appeared to have descended from upstairs and was standing unsteadily in front of us. Before he could change his mind, I swiftly entered the unlit hall and found a light switch.

A tall, apparently elderly man, totally dishevelled with thinning hair, and salt-and-pepper stubble of several weeks, was swaying and struggling to remain upright at the door. He was evidently incensed by the intrusion. Assisted by the minister, I managed to guide Mr McBain to his living room and sat him down. We remained patient despite a tirade of abusive protestations. Reluctantly and gradually he gave in, seeming eventually to accept the help at hand. A quick glance around the room showed cobwebs and patches of damp on the walls. The cold was overwhelming and the stench of the damp unmistakable. The antique furniture buried under clutter spoke loudly of neglect. I asked him for the location of the switch for the central heating system. He said that the boiler had broken down a few months earlier.

I was eventually permitted to do a physical examination. It would have been cruel to undress him in that cold house. My cursory assessment revealed low blood pressure, low pulse rate, anaemia, patches of bruising on his skin with spirally twisted body hair, puffy eye lids, and swollen wrists and ankles. It was not difficult to guess that Mr McBain had mild hypothermia, severe malnutrition, perhaps including scurvy, and needed urgent medical and social attention.

To my surprise, he agreed to come into hospital. We had only two kinds of ambulance service in Aberdeen – urgent with blue lights flashing and non-urgent, which could take up to several hours to attend. Rather than wait indefinitely for a non-urgent ambulance to arrive, I decided to take him in my car directly to my ward.

My diagnoses were confirmed. He was sixty-nine years old. He had borderline hypothermia and was malnourished. His rampant head lice created a panic among the young nurses and medical students. These problems aside, he had no other specific illness. He was self-neglect personified.

Mr McBain slowly improved over the next few days. At the weekly case conference, I was informed that he had vehemently refused to permit the social worker to arrange for cleaning of his house. He would not allow her to do any kind of assessment, as the means-tested system required that he pay for the services. He did not want the damp to be treated, nor the heating to be repaired. He would not see the occupational therapist, nor would he agree to 'home help'. To discharge him into existing conditions was not an option.

I had seen Mr McBain twice since admission. After the ward round that day I went specifically to see him once again. He was grateful for what I had done but was keen to go home. Reluctantly he spoke, not of depression, but inability to cope with the death of his wife. He admitted that having never looked after the house, he did not know how to do so. His wife used to manage that and the finances. Now everything cost so much, he was convinced that people were ripping him off. He had been saving for 'a rainy day', although he had come to believe that it was meaningless for him to live now that his beloved Eileen had passed away.

I encouraged him to talk more. Consumed by grief, he had been unable to return to work following his loss. He had been a very successful solicitor, financially secure, with no dependants, so he had been able to take early retirement. He had grown bored of his old friends and would pretend to be out whenever they called. Visits soon ceased. He felt safe and secure in the cocoon of the duvet. Lately, he had been boiling or baking potatoes and eating them with porridge only once a day. He did not want to employ a housekeeper. 'I need to save for a rainy day,' he repeated several times.

Very few among the strictly Calvinistic Scottish gentry ever believe that their life's savings should be spent on themselves. From an early age, children are taught, 'Always live within your means.' 'Any luxury must first be earned.' 'Savings are not to be touched.' 'Always save for a rainy day.' The 'rainy day' symbolises a catastrophe, an end, an event that is worse than anything one can imagine. I had had a few patients before who had failed to recognise the rain when it had been pouring. Mr McBain appeared to be such another.

It was clear that he had very strong views and would not change his mind easily. So I explained to him that he probably would have died in his sleep that night had I not brought him into hospital. That shook him a little but he said that he felt strong now. He promised to look after himself. He looked embarrassed that he had already talked too much and implored me to leave him alone.

With all the seriousness I could muster and hating myself for having to do this, I told him slowly that 'the rainy day' had arrived. At first he did not comprehend. I cannot forget his expression of pain, anguish and horror when he eventually realised what I meant. His lips quivered and he was silent for a long time. The realisation that he had indeed reached the brink of death hit him with a force for which he was not prepared. He stood up, took a few paces, came back, sat down and sighed a few times. I held his hand patiently when he broke down. Eventually, he whispered softly, 'What shall I do?'

I explained the various options available. It was a difficult decision for him to make. We finally agreed that he should temporarily stay in a very nice retirement home whilst his house was refurbished. The social worker and occupational therapists would access the house to see to all the necessary arrangements. He was discharged the following week.

Six weeks later in my Outpatient Clinic, Mr McBain was hardly recognisable. He looked several years younger, was well groomed and smartly dressed. He was still in the care home as his house repairs had not been completed. He liked it there and asked what I thought about him staying there for good. He did not have to worry about anything and had plenty of company. He had made new friends. He told me of one particular new friend, a widow who was living there temporarily until her son came to take her to Florida. She might stay in the home if he was there too.

I did not think that it was a good idea and I told him so. I suggested instead that he went round the world with his new friend and then returned to his refurbished house. His eyes began to sparkle but he did not say anything. I discharged him from my care, and he left murmuring his thanks.

It was heartening to receive a postcard from Miami a few months later. It simply read: 'Sunshine has followed the rainy day. Thanks and regards, George McBain, 22 Radislaw Avenue, Aberdeen.'

CHAPTER 22

Jack and Jessie

I drove past the cemetery as the sign indicated. I had to ask at the local shop for directions. And there it was at last, the house where the old man I had come to see lived alone.

I had finished my afternoon clinic at Fraserburgh Hospital and had dropped in to do a domiciliary visit on my way back to Aberdeen. It was opportune that the request by the local general practitioner had arrived just before I had started off for Fraserburgh. Although there was no urgency about the visit, I could save three hours and a round trip of eighty miles by visiting him that day.

The fishing village of Sandhaven, adjacent to the town of Fraserburgh, looked grim with deprivation and neglect amidst the signs of past prosperity when the catch had been good and the fleet, large. It had once been the envy of most of the other fishing communities on that north eastern shore of the Moray Firth. The old man's house was situated behind a disused cold-storage plant. It was close to the beach, which here was full of boulders and brambles, in contrast to other parts nearby that were covered with soft golden sand.

There was a wooden ramp leading to the front door. It was rather steep and beginning to rot. I buzzed the front doorbell several times. I could hear voices inside but no-one came. I walked around the outside of the house to see if there was another entrance. The vast expanse of sea, visible unrestricted from the back of the house, was breathtaking and hypnotic. The back porch was at a slight elevation and I had to jump to reach the concrete platform. The wide oceanic vista was even more impressive from this height. The door into the kitchen opened when I tried it. 'Hello, Mr Burns,' I repeatedly shouted while entering, adding, 'I am the doctor from the hospital.' My calls were buried beneath the loud noises echoing through the house. Mr Burns did not respond. No-one did.

I walked inside. A Comprehensive Geriatric Assessment begins at the first contact. A quick glance around told me, yet again, the familiar story of the poverty-stricken pensioner. The ancient gas cooker was filthy and rusty. The kitchen units were frayed, showing the compressed sawdust inside the door panels. An unopened loaf of bread sat beside a filthy torn towel on the small kitchen table. Walking towards the open door, which probably led to a short corridor, I noticed that the door panel of one of the kitchen units had fallen off its hinges. The exposed shelf was stacked with tins of tuna, sardines and soup. No wonder the man was losing weight. What an irony it was that someone in one of the most well-known Scottish fishing ports was surviving on tinned sardines imported from the Philippines.

The corridor was dark. I followed the noise to find its source was a blaring television. The room was darkened by closed curtains. I called out once again. The room was so cluttered that it took me a few seconds to spot the wheelchair. I was reaching towards it when I saw an undefined object heaped on the floor. It was Mr Burns.

I pulled back the curtain. The bright sunlight pervaded the dank stuffy room and allowed me to locate the television switch. I turned it off. I went over to Mr Burns. He looked at me but could only produce a hoarse whisper. My ears had not accommodated to his way of speaking as yet. I tried to lift him from the floor and found that he was remarkably light. Then I remembered.

The referral letter had said that he was a bilateral amputee. The GP, Dr Gould, had not mentioned deafness, but he had written, 'Jack has not responded to treatment for depression for the past three months. He is getting worse, continuing to lose weight and has become totally dependent. I would appreciate it if any organic cause could be ruled out before asking the psychiatric services to intervene. He is a proud and uncomplaining man. Routine bloods are normal.' I gently placed Mr Burns half-reclining on a tired-looking sofa which was spilling plastic foam. My ears had started to function as I heard the whisper, 'Thank you, Doctor.' I sat on his electric wheelchair near him. The tyres were flat. Slowly and with great patience I was able to glean a history.

He had been expecting me. My secretary had telephoned him that morning to let him know that I would be arriving around four PM. It was indeed about that time that I had reached his front door, but he had not heard my knock. He had been startled by me entering through the kitchen. He could not explain how he had fallen from the wheelchair whilst trying to investigate the sound he had heard. He had then been unable to get up and had been crying out for help. Since his voice was no more than a whisper, I had not heard him. He was agitated and embarrassed. A quick look at him told me that only his pride had been hurt by the fall. Slowly he composed himself.

He was seventy-one years of age. He had been quite well until about six months before, when he had started to feel increasingly tired for no reason. He would wake up with an aching body. He had once made models of warships from do-it-yourself kits. Now he was not interested in doing even that. He did not feel like doing anything. When the GP insisted that he needed to keep busy, he had tried again. His hands would shake violently while trying to pick up the tiny bits of the model with tweezers. Placing them appropriately had proved too much of an effort and he had given up. He felt that he had become very slow. Getting in and out of bed was proving to be a great problem, so he had lately taken to sleeping in the wheelchair itself. A home-help had been employed since the previous month. He had given her the spare key as she had complained that he took too much time to let her in. He had not been out of his house for the past three months. He had finally listened to the advice of his GP and consented to see a specialist, but had refused to go to the hospital, vowing to die in his own house.

At the time of the the Second World War he had been a young man. He was commissioned to the Royal Navy and soon promoted to the rank of Able Seaman. He was considered something of an expert in wireless communications and in laying mines on the seabed. His frigate had destroyed a number of German U-boats in the English Channel. He was commended. Then came the day when one of the U-boats somehow managed to escape and nearly destroyed the frigate. He was plucked from the sea, floating on a raft of splintered wood, minus three quarters of his right leg. It was a miracle that he had survived. It took over six months in Portsmouth to regain his health. Rather than accept an honourable discharge, he asked to be re-assigned for active duty as before, much against the wishes of Jessie, the wee lassie from Govan who had nursed him back to health. His job was such that he did not need a leg, he told his commanding officer.

All went well for the next two years. Then the day before the Normandy landing they were spotted by a German plane patrolling the Channel and got hit. The blast took a chunk off his left thigh. Writing long letters to Jessie from his hospital bed in Southampton saved his mind. The wound subsequently turned septic and his left leg had to be amputated. Jessie somehow managed to get a transfer to Southampton hospital to be with him. He was discharged on the day the war ended. They married that same day.

Mr Burns returned to Fraserburgh with his bride. He worked in the local telephone exchange until he retired. Jessie cleaned and filleted fish, quickly rising to the rank of supervisor.

The couple had moved into this council bungalow twenty years before for its view of the sea. They bought it for themselves fourteen years later. After another twelve months Jessie started to swell up. It was her heart. He woke one morning to find her lying cold beside him. He realised that she was dead. She was buried in the local cemetery on the way to the village. He had visited her grave every day until this illness struck.

I felt a surge of strange emotions go through me. I was looking at this shell of a shrivelled old man, whispering calmly to describe the ferocity of a horrific war and acts of unparalleled bravery. At the same time, I could sense the immense love, tenderness and devotion of the young lovers. I shivered and vowed to make him better. The nation was obliged to do so, I thought. How often does one come across a real-life hero? I looked at the framed photograph of a bright and happy bride proudly pushing a naval seaman in a wheelchair. I had never before encountered such profound love and sacrifice.

His symptoms – the stiffening of his body, the softening of his voice, the tremors in his hands and the slowness of his movements – all pointed to Parkinson's disease. I examined him thoroughly. He did look depressed and weak. It was no surprise that Dr Gould reckoned he had depression, but I did not think that was the primary problem. I looked for the objective signs of Parkinson's disease. It was difficult to find them at first but the glabellar tap, cogwheel rigidity and tremors of the tongue were all there. Whilst putting him back in his wheelchair, I assured him that he would soon get better with treatment.

He obviously did not believe me. 'I know Jessie is calling me,' he said.

I had spent a very long time with him already. It would be difficult to explain Parkinson's disease in a hurry. He was going to need a lot of information and encouragement to believe my words. Hence I thought it best that Dr Gould should talk through the diagnosis and treatment.

'I'll discuss the treatment with your general practitioner and he will visit you soon,' I said. Before leaving, I asked for his permission to look around the house.

It was a typical ex-council two-bed bungalow. This was Mrs Thatcher's double-edged strategy. By selling the old houses that needed repair and refurbishment the councils could save a lot of money. The tenants who bought them at giveaway prices would feel proud property owners, little realising that they would need to spend their lives' savings on the deal. Jessie had died before she had had time to refurbish the house. Jack had lost the will to do anything after her death. It was no surprise that it was in such a state of disrepair.

The flooring was old pile carpet with loose rugs to cover the worn-out areas. The sofa was too soft and low to transfer to from the wheelchair. The central heating was turned up too high. The bed was a repository for all kinds of clothing and junk. The bath was a cast-iron enamelled white tub, which had turned brown and black at the bottom. There was no shower. There was no hand-rail. The toilet seat was chipped; the cover and flush handle were broken. The fridge contained a fresh bottle of milk and a few eggs. I made a mental note of all this.

I let myself out into the cool evening. The sun had set but the eastern sky was glowing with a myriad of pink, yellow and red colours reminding me of the Northern Lights. I got into my car and started to dictate several letters. The first was to the general practitioner advising him that Mr Burns was suffering from Parkinson's disease and not depression. I recommended treatment and asked to see Mr Burns after two months for follow-up. I also asked whether Dr Gould could arrange for him to have a hearing aid. Then I wrote a letter to the Director of Social Services informing him that he had a war hero living under appalling conditions in his county. I advised him to assign a social worker to Mr Burns who would arrange the necessary services. I dictated another letter to the Community Occupational Therapist asking her to do an urgent home assessment visit. I explained that I had found Mr Burns fallen on the floor. He was at great risk and something had to be done very quickly. He needed considerable adaptations and modifications to his house for safety. I also asked whether the electric buggy could be serviced. It was nearly seven o'clock by the time I had finished dictating. It would be at least two more hours before I reached home.

I saw Mr Burns two months later in his house. The old wooden ramp had gone. There was now a gently sloping concrete ramp with a handrail on one side leading to the front door. He came to open the door promptly. He was dressed in a navy blue blazer showing the badge of his division over the breast pocket. He had a neck scarf, and a beret on his head. He shook my hand firmly and motioned me inside. I approved of the new floor covering. It was a firm industrial carpet which made it easy to manoeuvre the wheelchair. The old furniture and clutter had been removed.

I did not have to ask how he was, but did so as a matter of politeness.

He was fine and had been busy constructing 'the Invincible'. He was also waiting for his hearing aid.

'I do my own messages [shopping],' he said, following my gaze to the fresh flowers next to Jessie's photograph. 'I bought those from Spar,' he added. He was not whispering any more.

He offered me a cup of tea with biscuits on the back porch. It would have been unthinkable to refuse this honour. We both enjoyed the view in silence and sipped our tea. He looked at me intently, took my hand and said, 'Jessie will have to wait a little longer, ken?' I nodded.

It was then time for me to return home. I decided to use his facilities before leaving for Aberdeen. The bath had been replaced by a walk-in shower, the commode was new and there were grab rails on the wall. He wheeled himself easily to the car to see me off. The tyres had been properly inflated. I must remember to thank the Occupational Therapist, I thought.

I had an almost irresistible urge on my way to stop by the cemetery and visit Jessie's grave. I was sure it would have a simple headstone. I would be able to identify it easily because Jack would have placed fresh flowers there. I wanted to tell her that Jack would be OK, but I didn't. I pressed the accelerator instead.

CHAPTER 23

The Mind Reader

'I thought you might like to have these,' she said. 'My late husband loved these things.'

I looked at the neat pile of objects on her side table. A silver tot (a measure for whisky), a slim cigarette case, a samovar, a framed pencil sketch of some famous mosque by an obscure artist, another signed original black and white ink sketch of some birds, and an ornate carved wooden Chinese bowl. I did not know what to say. She obviously had no idea that mosques and whisky tots do not go together, and neither did I, who am a Hindu and not a Muslim.

'Why are you giving these to me?' I asked. I was annoyed and felt very uncomfortable about accepting them.

'Take them home and don't ask silly questions,' she said and concentrated all her attention on my daughter Meena. The two of them started to sing a silly limerick and then disappeared into the garden to play. I looked at Leela who was placing the items carefully into a handily positioned plastic bag in order to pacify the old lady. We never talked of those things again.

I suspected that the pencil sketches could be worth something some day. The greedy part of me, however, made me say to myself that the combined worth of all these items in a junk shop would be less than £10, the limit of the value of gifts from patients that we were allowed to keep for ourselves. So I did not think it necessary to hand the gifts over to the hospital. I wrote a letter thanking her for them. I said that I had accepted them as a one-off gift from a friend. I explained that as I did not treat her privately, I would have to hand over any future presents to the hospital. I added that I would not be able to accept them because it might be construed that I was taking advantage of her vulnerable condition. Begging her not to give me anything more in the future, I suggested that she could support some charitable cause instead. She never acknowledged my letter. The bag remained, unopened, for a very long time in the loft of my house.

Rosie was a remarkable woman. I first met her at her home, on a visit requested by her general practitioner. I forget if there was a specific complaint. I think it was for a Comprehensive Geriatric Assessment as she was eighty-four years of age, lived alone and had been having problems with mobility. She had been a widow for several years and had no children.

'Enter. The door is open,' instructed a clear, authoritative female voice in response to my knock at her door. I remember seeing her reclining on a chaise longue on that first visit to her house. 'Forgive me, won't you, for not letting you in. It is my knee, you see,' she said, extending her hand. 'Does she expect me to kiss it?' I wondered, shaking it limply.

A small ornate wooden table beside her held a number of things, including a box of boiled sweets. I was a little put off by her rather imperious manner. She reminded me of the so-called *memsahibs* of bygone colonial days. I took a detailed medical history. Our conversation that day was far from being particularly cordial. Her suspicious glances, sharp tongue and barbed comments, with no attempt at cooperation, irritated me. I had to struggle to hide my inner feelings. She indicated that it was her left knee which was very painful. The right would also become painful at times. She blamed the knees for her obesity; she was a big lady. I examined her with difficulty but as thoroughly as I could. She was about five-foot eight inches tall and must have weighed at least eighteen stone. She had great difficulty in standing from a sitting position. Once standing, she could walk with the support of a zimmer frame. She could limp to the stairlift in order to access her bedroom. I inspected her living conditions, kitchen, toilet and bedroom. An old-fashioned potty was in the latter, although she could manage to get into her en suite bathroom slowly. The house was large with rich artefacts and fine furniture.

Eventually, after two uncomfortable hours with this uncooperative patient, I was ready to leave. 'Dr Gould will be in touch with you shortly. You will need to have a few X-rays, a scan of your heart, some blood tests and an ECG,' I informed her. 'I will be discussing your treatment with him this evening,' I said.

'So, what can you do for me then, Doctor?' she asked. Was she mocking me, I wondered.

'I do not think that I can do anything for you. But I can help you to help yourself, if you wish,' I blurted out. I could not have been more candid or cruel, but I had had enough of her.

I still remember the curious expression that came over her face. She was rich. She was big. She was important in the community. I doubted whether anybody had ever before dared to tell her off. She was clearly taken aback by my impudence. 'Sit down,' she commanded. I waited but did not sit down. Slowly, she said in a soft voice, 'What do I have to do?' The abject terror in her voice was now unmistakable. I sat down.

I explained to her that several things were less than satisfactory. In particular, that it was her weight which was causing the trouble with her knees and not the other way around. Her blood pressure was a little high. The swelling in her ankles and her shortness of breath on exertion could be early signs of mild heart failure, which needed to be investigated and treated if necessary. They could alternatively be due to immobility and obesity. Without any pretence at being kind, I went on to explain that she needed to change her dietary habits, lose weight, become independent and focus on getting better.

'I hardly eat anything. I am not able to exercise and so I have put on weight,' came the usual response. It was not the first time I had heard similar excuses from other patients.

'I am told that even the disabled people in Ethiopia are very thin,' I retorted, looking at the pile of National Geographic magazines on a bookshelf. She glared at me as I silently stood my ground. We understood each other. She then capitulated. Could I please suggest a diet for her?

I recommended a menu of green vegetables, fish and chicken. A number of her favourite foods were prohibited, namely eggs, potatoes, bread, desserts, boiled sweets and wine. I asked her to come and see me in my outpatient clinic in three months' time for a follow-up. She appeared to listen to me but the expression of incredulity did not leave her face. I made my exit half an hour later. I was almost certain that I had been wasting my time and that our next meeting would be in an orthopaedic ward where she would be being treated for a fractured hip. I wrote a detailed letter to her general practitioner and forgot all about her.

I was going through the medical records of the ten patients who were due to attend my outpatient clinic that day. I came across her file. There was a letter from Dr Gould informing me that all the preliminary tests had been normal. My Registrar had acknowledged that letter and hence I had not been reminded of her. My feeling was that she would not be attending that day and I fully expected to receive an apology.

I could not have been more wrong.

Rosie walked into my consulting room with the help of a walking stick. She looked different. She had lost three stone in weight in three and half months. She was smiling kindly when she told me that there was not a day when she did not curse me during her meal times. I laughed and asked her to continue to give me her blessings. She laughed loudly. She had become lively, had started to write poetry, and had sacked her accountant. She was now doing all the book-keeping for the farm she owned herself. We agreed that she should be referred for knee replacement when she reached her target weight of thirteen stone over the next two months. I apologised to her for being so nasty at our last meeting. She smiled brightly and said that a good medicine was always bitter. She put her hand on my shoulder and stood up.

Two months later I was most surprised to find her on my ward. She had been admitted with an attack of fast irregular heart beat – that is, rapid atrial fibrillation. Mercifully she did not take long to recover and it did not prevent her having her knee operation. She stuck to her diet and reached her target weight. I was then able to refer her to the orthopaedic surgeon and offered to rehabilitate her on my ward after the knee replacement. By the time she had the surgery she had lost a further stone. The six weeks of rehabilitation under my care gave me an opportunity to get to know her a great deal better. I became quite fond of her. She always had some cheeky remark for me. Before walking out of my ward on the day her rehabilitation was complete she told all the other patients how fortunate they were to have me as their Consultant Physician. I was embarrassed.

It was a few weeks later that I got a thank-you card from her. She was well. She no longer needed the stairlift and could manage some light gardening. She would like to invite me, Leela and our daughter Meena to lunch at her house, which she would prepare herself. I was to choose the day so that there could be no possibility of refusal. In fact Leela chose the day and had a long chat with Rosie on the telephone. It was after the meal that day that she presented the gifts to me.

Leela and Meena took to her instantly. The three of them developed a special fondness for one another. They would correspond and exchange small gifts. She was a very kind person. She continued to send birthday presents to Meena even though I protested; she asked if there was any law against it. I did not argue with her. A few years passed. My family maintained their friendship with her through cards at Christmas and birthdays.

I needed to sponsor a young student in Nepal to go to Karachi to read Medicine. This was going to cost £3000. I toyed with the idea of asking Rosie to provide the sponsorship, but I could not bring myself to do so. Even though it was a little hard for me, I provided the money myself.

I was no longer employed by Grampian Health Authority in Aberdeen when the news of Rosie's death reached me in Barrow-in-Furness. It was a shock for us all. She had died suddenly whilst tending her garden. She was ninety years old. I was unable to attend her funeral, but Leela went.

Several months later, a letter arrived from a firm of solicitors. I was informed that a cheque for £3000, bequeathed by Rosie, would be arriving for me within a few weeks. There was no message.

CHAPTER 24

The Death of a Cat

I settled down at my desk, nursing a cup of coffee and scanning through the pile of paperwork before me. Buried within the heap I came across the following telephone message, marked urgent.

> Time of message: 10.46 am.
> Message taken by: Irene.
>
> **Jock McEwen, 17 Clarence Drive, Bridge of Dee, Aberdeen, 65+**
> I think he is very ill and I can't find his GP. He is refusing to let me in. Can you help? There is very bad smell. The environmental health people will visit.
> *Joanne Seymour, Senior Social Worker*

I looked at my watch. It was just after eleven AM.

I had known Jo for several years. She was sharp, decisive and efficient, with patient care firmly prioritised above paperwork. I had learnt a great deal from her and respected her professional opinion. The patient was aged over sixty-six years, thus qualifying for the services of our specialty. I asked Irene to telephone her and let her know that I would be visiting Mr McEwen within the hour.

It was twenty-minutes by car from the hospital to Clarence Drive. This was part of a run-down council housing estate constructed in haste during the early 1960s. Row upon row of two-up two-down match-box houses stretched into the distance, many in need of repair and a coat of paint. Evident squalor, overgrown grass verges, the excreta of ferocious rotweilers and alsatians, and a mushrooming of satellite antennae showed this to be typical of most deprived areas in Britain. (New university campuses, a supermarket, a sports complex and smart executive housing have since transformed this area completely.)

It was good to find Jo waiting at the front door. She informed me that she had responded to a call from a neighbour who thought it strange that Mr McEwen, 'Jock', had not been seen for a few days yet his front door was not locked. Being the duty Social Worker for that day, she had come straight away. Jock had responded to her knock by shouting at her to go away and then, suddenly, had become very quiet. She had dared to push the front door open but had been confronted by darkness and a horrible stench. Alone and reluctant to venture further inside, she had returned to her office to contact me and the Environmental Health Department. She had returned a few minutes earlier to wait for me.

Calling out loudly and pushing the buzzer for long moments, we entered the house. The smell was overpowering. There was no answer. The interior was dark; the electricity seemed to have been cut. A window became vaguely visible prompting Jo to pull the curtain and open the window for some fresh air.

A man with an unkempt beard was lying on a sofa, half covered by a tartan travelling rug. He appeared to be unconscious. The place was filthy. Next to him lay the decaying body of a cat, which seemed to be the source of the smell. I rushed to the man. He was breathing and his pulse was strong. I called to him and put gentle pressure on his breast bone with my hand. He opened his eyes and grumbled, 'Go away', pushing away my hand. The look of shock and horror visible on Jo's face must have been reflected on my own. The ABC (airway, breathing, circulation) and GCS (Glasgow Coma Scale) assessments thus completed,

I called Irene on my mobile phone to send an ambulance straight away, although it would not need to be in emergency mode with flashing blue lights.

Jock glared at me without comprehension when I informed him that he would be going to hospital. Refusals began when the message eventually registered with him. An attempt to rise in protest failed as the strain took hold and his head slumped down on the settee. He appeared to black out, but seconds later was bombarding us with a torrent of abuse. I needed some fresh air to combat the nausea and dizziness brought on by the stench. From my vantage point beside the window I began to inspect the surroundings.

Before me lay squalor of immense proportions. This looked like a case of Diogenes syndrome. Also known as 'senile squalor syndrome', this is often seen in elderly people. The name is, however, misleading. Diogenes was a cynic in the fourth century BC, a recluse who shunned all worldly possessions. Whichever geriatrician coined the name for this syndrome was being cynical himself. The cardinal feature is the hoarding of objects; patients never throw anything away. I had witnessed several extreme examples; this was not the most severe.

The living room was cluttered and filthy. A small coffee table with a broken leg, a television on its stand in one corner and a stuffed bookcase were present in addition to the long settee. The cat was a plump brown and white animal, which had probably been dead for a week. There were stacks of old newspapers and magazines spilling into the kitchen. Here, beside the cat flap, was a bowl of solidified milk and an empty tin of cat food. The fridge held an ancient bottle of milk, a greening loaf of bread and some furred jars of jam. The four burners of the gas cooker were caked in burnt food. There were dozens more empty tins of cat food on a shelf; the rest of the shelves held grimy pots and pans.

The bedroom was full of junk. The bathroom was filthy. The toilet was un-flushed and the bathtub overflowed with toiletries. The landing bore several tea chests, balanced precariously in a tower.

Jo was green with nausea when I returned to the living room. She rushed outside to gulp the fresh air. I followed her to discuss the case. There was no doubt that Jock needed hospitalisation for a comprehensive geriatric assessment. Meanwhile, the Environmental Health people needed to inspect the house. The dead cat had to be removed. Then the house needed to be thoroughly cleaned and refurbished in part. Both of us were surprised that a person could have been living in such conditions in a wealthy city like Aberdeen, which was well known for its excellent social services.

Many questions remained unanswered. Who had been bringing food to the house? When was the last time someone had seen him? I began to suspect that this was not a case of Diogenes syndrome after all. My previous patients had been mobile and eccentric old men and women. Had I made a wrong diagnosis?

The ambulance soon arrived. The paramedics were nervous when Jock fainted whilst they were trying to lift him. They had never experienced anything like this. He was taken to my assessment ward at Woodend Hospital. I was not a popular man among the nurses that day for bringing in a patient in that state.

Cleaning and examining him proved to be difficult. Jock's verbal abuse towards all nurses and doctors persisted. Any attempt at raising his head more than twenty degrees made him faint promptly. He was emaciated, mildly anaemic and dehydrated. He did not show any signs of internal bleeding. There were no other localising signs except I could feel hard masses in his sigmoid colon, no doubt due to chronic constipation. Physical examination revealed two pressure sores, one on his bottom and another on his left hip. All the muscles in his arms and legs had atrophied through lack of use. He was treated with intravenous normal saline and slept well through the night.

By the following morning, although his blood pressure had returned to normal while lying down, it continued to drop severely when he sat up. On raising his head, his systolic blood pressure would drop to 40 mm Hg (the normal level is 120 mm Hg) and precipitate a 'syncope' or faint. His foul vocabulary re-commenced whenever he was disturbed. He refused to give any information about himself and how he had got into the state in which Jo and I had found him. After the third attempt, he stopped fighting the insertion of a naso-gastric tube. I later discovered that our intern had inserted this by keeping Jock's head raised. Jock must have soon realised the futility of his struggles.

Several days passed and we remained none-the-wiser about the course of events that had led up to Jock's admission, nor about Jock himself. He had no visitors. An initial psychiatric assessment was unhelpful. I began to suspect that he had decided to kill himself by refusing to eat and drink and had confined himself to the sofa for several weeks. That his cat had died in his arms must have surely reinforced his resolve to die. Now, in hospital, he did not seem to care or to be aware of anything. He remained unable to sit up and was nursed in bed. All we could do was simply replenish his nutrients and calories and hope for a break.

I was in my office when a Staff Nurse from my ward telephoned with an interesting development. A Mrs Betty Henderson had come to visit Jock and was demanding to see me. Hoping that this visitor would provide some information, I agreed to see her straight away and hurried to the ward.

A middle aged, neatly dressed woman stood alone in the interview room. She was courteous and well mannered. She provided the following story.

She lived in the same neighbourhood as Jock. She had returned from holiday to discover that he had been taken into hospital. Jock had been an architect. He had taken early retirement to care for his wife Angela, when she developed a brain tumour. Half of her body had become paralysed following surgery for the tumour. He had devoted himself to her care during the last two years of her life. The couple had had no children.

He had been overcome with grief following Angela's burial. He would visit the cemetery for hours, return home, lie on his settee and stare vacantly at the television. Some days he would buy cat food and other provisions from the corner shop on his way back from the cemetery. Betty lived in the same neighbourhood as Jock and sometimes popped round with home cooked food. He would eat, say thank you, and then be consumed by his thoughts. She would stay with him for a while and then return home. She described Jock as one of the nicest men she had ever met. 'Look after him well, Doctor,' she implored as she left.

Did I detect a special fondness for him or was she just being a good neighbour? The new information supported my suspicion that he was trying to end his own life. I had never before come across such a severe grief reaction. The death of his cat must have been the final straw.

Jock remained on my ward, where his general health began to improve. He would suck at a straw whilst lying down to take milk or fruit juice. The pressure sores healed. His urinary catheter was removed and he remained continent. He was having bowel motions. His mood began to lift. He even stopped swearing and managed an occasional smile. Nurses now felt able to sit and talk with him, interaction which he appeared to enjoy. He confirmed his age to be sixty-six years and gave the name of his GP whom he had never had to visit. He did not have any records in the hospital. He had been a very healthy man all his life.

His postural hypotension (low blood pressure on raising his head), however, remained a problem and he could not sit up. Searching through the scientific literature, I had been unable to find a similar case, although it was well documented that starvation and malnutrition could cause failure of the autonomic nervous system. Passive exercises of the arms and legs, compression stockings and slight elevation of the head-end of bed made no improvement. Steroids initiated manic symptoms so were promptly stopped. In desperation I decided to try an unconventional treatment. If it were today, with all its restrictions on the practice of medicine, I wonder whether it would have been allowed at all.

I had a long chat with Jock. He too wanted to be able to walk and be independent once again. He was prepared to suffer the discomfort of my proposed treatment, although I could not give him full assurance that I would succeed. I arranged a special case conference to discuss him. Present were Jock, myself, a few junior doctors, the head physiotherapist and her colleague, the occupational therapist, the ward sister, and Jock's named nurse. I explained that although Jock had improved considerably he still suffered from severe postural hypotension and no medication had been able to cure him. I had a feeling that it was due to his severe malnutrition and alarming loss of weight ('cachexia') at the time of admission. Now that everything was almost normal, we had to reset his baro-receptors, that is, his internal gauge of his own blood pressure. My colleagues had no problem believing me thus far. I asked if anyone had any suggestions as to how to proceed and was greeted with blank, expectant faces.

I explained my strategy. I proposed that he should be nursed in bed, initially tilted at an angle of thirty degrees. Thereafter, the incline should be increased by five degrees each week. Jock had agreed to this strategy, resolving any ethical considerations with his unwavering consent. It was agreed that there was nothing to lose.

Considerable modifications to his bed were made by the occupational therapist, physiotherapist and ward sister. It took six weeks for him to be able tolerate an incline of forty-five degrees. He could now feed himself and read newspapers without having to lift them above his head. Maintaining him at sixty degrees proved to be quite a task. Straps, belts, wooden blocks and pillows were employed so that he would not slide down whilst asleep. At seventy degrees he did not faint. Then he rebelled and wanted to stand upright. Ten weeks had passed and the moment of truth had arrived. I checked his blood pressure while he reclined on the bed. With strong support he eased himself to his feet and to everyone's delight did not faint. Two nurses and the physiotherapist held him upright while I checked his blood pressure. Systolic pressure remained at 90 mm Hg; it had dropped by 30 only. Smiles all round.

For the next few weeks, Jock was taken to the gymnasium and its tilting table. He was raised to the vertical several times per visit, each manoeuvre lasting for a few minutes. He began to walk slowly and could sleep on a normal bed once again.

In the mean time, Jo had arranged for a complete clearance of his house. The stained carpet and settee were removed. A coat of paint and new floor covering, along with some new furniture, were procured. The kindly neighbour helped with the renovations. The frequency of her visits to the hospital increased remarkably once Jock had begun to sit up and could look into her eyes. Nearly five months later, Jock returned home with Jo and the Occupational Therapist. This initial visit went well and I gave the all-clear for his final discharge. It was a memorable occasion when he walked out of the ward wearing new clothes brought by Betty.

Three months later Jock and Betty arrived in my outpatient clinic. He looked well and there was no drop in his blood pressure when he stood up. Betty's beaming smile told me that Jock's autonomic nervous system was functioning very well indeed. I never saw them again.

CHAPTER 25

She Would Not Have Come

Every medical student is taught that, 'If you make a rare diagnosis, you are rarely right'. The correct way of arriving at a diagnosis is to recognise the pattern, think of common things first, and fit every sign and symptom into a disease process. In spite of adhering to this system, we can all make mistakes. However, we manage to cover ourselves by never committing totally at first. This helps to maintain the essential objectivity in the doctor-patient relationship. We develop a shield of self-preservation by avoiding dogmatic and definite statements and produce a list of probabilities called differential diagnoses. Even for the patient, a little doubt expressed by the doctor can sometimes confer a little hope. The final diagnosis becomes clear only after all the tests and reports. Things can go disastrously wrong if this system is breached.

My patient was extremely nervous and apprehensive, convinced that she had cancer and was doomed to an imminent death. 'Have I got cancer?' she asked for the second time within the first two minutes of the consultation. Patiently, I repeated that I needed to examine her and do some tests before I could answer her questions.

'I am sure I am going to die like Millie,' she said without paying any attention to what I was saying. I looked at her husband, pleading for help.

'Stop it. Let the doctor do his job first,' the man sternly told his wife. This quietened her momentarily and she eyed me with suspicion.

Mrs Ellie Gibson, accompanied by her husband, had come to see me privately from Speyside. She had some tingling in both feet and felt occasional numbness in her right hand. She had been dropping things, could not easily fasten her buttons, and had fallen a few times. She felt rotten but had been avoiding her GP for fear that he would confirm her suspicion of cancer. Until three months before she had been riding horses, doing all the gardening, going for long walks and had been the picture of health and vitality at the age of seventy-eight.

She had had several falls from horses in the days when she used to train them and take part in show-jumping. She had once, many years before, had to wear a collar. She had had no other illnesses in the past. Her mother had died aged seventy-eight, when she had been found to have a brain tumour. Her only sibling, Millie, had also died at this age of leukaemia, two years earlier. Their parents had bred horses in Shrewsbury and the girls had helped. Millie had been a fine horse-woman and a good trainer. She had never got married and had inherited the farm. Tom was a gallant young tax inspector whom Ellie had met and married within three months. He was a few years younger than her. They had had no children. They had moved to Scotland on Tom's retirement about ten years before.

'We are "white settlers",' he said. This derogatory phrase was used by the ignorant Scottish nationalists resentful of those English who would pay generously to buy a retirement place in the beautiful Scottish countryside. The local villagers would smirk at them and then talk behind their backs in the village shop, although the grocer and the postmaster would be the first to take their money, often paid at a higher rate than the locals. Most people like them would pretend not to have noticed these racial jibes for the sake of peace. We talked about this and laughed while waiting for Ellie to get undressed for examination.

Tom said that they were vegetarians, did not smoke and made their own wine. He liked the excellent local single malt but Ellie hardly touched hard liquor. Neither of them was on any medication. He painted in water-colour whilst Ellie wrote poetry. They kept each other company and rarely had visitors from England.

A classic presentation of cervical myelopathy, I thought to myself. This is a very common condition in elderly people. The spinal cord in the neck becomes affected resulting in weakness of the limbs. Another possibility was that the old neck injury could have caused an osteophyte growth over the years and herniated a cervical disc, causing pressure on Ellie's spinal cord. The differential diagnosis also included late-onset multiple sclerosis, as she had also given a history of intermittent symptoms. In addition, there was always the possibility of a stroke at this age, which could show itself in a variety of ways.

'Come and confirm my worst suspicions, Doctor,' she said from behind the curtain. I examined her. She was well preserved, except for her hands which showed evidence of osteoarthritis. There were no lumps or bumps anywhere in her body. There were no signs of cardiovascular disease. Her chest sounded clear. Her abdomen was flat and normal. The tendon reflexes in her right arm were absent contrasting with exaggerated knee and up-going plantar reflexes. Her neck movements were severely restricted. I felt a profound sense of relief that my initial suspicions were likely to be correct.

'Did you find it?' she asked. I knew that she was asking me whether I had found cancer. I was well aware how the news of cancer in a sibling affects an individual. My elder brother had narrowly survived the removal of three-quarters of his right lung and was having radiotherapy for cancer in the remainder. I shuddered at the memory of our seemingly endless telephone conversations when he would talk of his fear of impending death. Is this what made me breach my objectivity?

'No, there is no cancer,' I told her. 'But I have not finished yet,' I said, asking her permission for a digital rectal examination. Again the result was negative, as was the check for occult bleeding. I asked if she had noticed any bleeding from the front passage, which she denied. I had given her a very thorough physical examination.

'Well? Give us the verdict,' she demanded. 'How long have I got?'

'I think you have arthritis in your neck. Your old neck injuries appear to be showing now. The spinal cord is being compressed. This should get better with an operation. It can be cured. There is no cancer at all,' I told her.

She was speechless. With both of her hands tightly gripping my right wrist, she tried to have a good look at me but was not successful due to the relief flooding down from both her eyes. I hastily went out of the cubicle and started to wash my hands furiously.

Tom had heard me. 'What good news, Doctor. Thank you,' he said. He asked me about the next step in her management. I explained that I would be referring her to Mr John Walters, the neurosurgeon. I knew that he was very good. 'One of the best in the country,' I said.

Eli emerged from the cubicle and asked about further tests. She still had not fully accepted that she did not have leukaemia. I took a sample of her blood and arranged for her to have a chest X-ray. I explained that these were just routine tests prior to an operation. I also explained that she would need an MR scan of her neck which would be organised by the neurosurgeon in due course.

'Are you sure there is no cancer, Doctor?'

'Yes, Mrs Gibson, I am positive. I will ring you with the report of the blood test. You go home and stop worrying.' I shook her hand confidently.

Two days later I telephoned her to confirm that the blood tests were indeed normal and she did not have leukaemia. I explained that the chest x-ray report was not yet available. I was assured that it would be sent to Mr Walters directly in time for her appointment. Yes, I had personally spoken with Mr Walters and he would see her in two days' time. I would be arranging an appointment for her to come and see me again in due course.

'I can't thank you enough, Doctor,' she said and put the phone down.

I received a detailed letter from John Walters the following week. He had little to add to my clinical findings. However, the MR scan had shown considerable destruction of the body of the third and fourth cervical vertebrae by a soft tissue mass indenting the spinal cord. He also thought that there was a rounded shadow behind the heart, probably the site of the primary lung cancer. He had referred Mrs Gibson to Jim Cassidy for a bronchoscopy. Palliative radiotherapy was being planned for her neck.

I had been carried away by my confidence in my own ability to make a diagnosis. I had recognised the pattern. I had managed to fit all the signs and symptoms into a single disease process. I had thought of the possible differential diagnoses. I had done everything by the book; yet I had committed a cardinal mistake.

Someone who had never smoked had developed a cancer in her lung. This had already spread to her neck bones, causing compression of the spinal cord. The resulting nervous weakness had brought her to me seeking help. This was indeed most uncommon. I had given her false assurance, believing in the old adage but forgetting my own objectivity. This was unpardonable.

I cannot forget those eyes which once overflowed with relief and gratitude. They must have seen me very clearly indeed once she had heard the full story. I could not bring myself to ask her to come and see me again. I have told myself time and time again that she probably would not have come.

CHAPTER 26

Looking Forward

Barrow-in-Furness, 4 AM, August 1978

'Could I speak to Professor Krumowski, please? This is Dr Gautam from England. I wish to speak to him about his mother.'

'I will get him for you,' a woman's voice said. I held on.

'Leon here,' said a new voice. 'How is she, Doctor?'

'Not very well, I am afraid'.

A long pause ensued.

'Is she going to make it?'

'It's not likely but I have seen miracles. We could pray.'

'I will take the next flight.'

'She has been asking for you. I will tell her. Thank you.'

I was speaking to Professor Leon Krumowski of the University of Music in Halifax, Canada. His mother, suffering from chronic renal failure, had been admitted in a critical condition to our hospital. She had not been able to produce any urine for several hours. Her blood urea levels were astronomical (101.9 mmol/litre when the normal level is 5–7 mmol/litre). She was 78 years of age but was mentally alert and had been managing by herself, up until this crisis, at her home in

Coniston. She appeared to be septic due to a urinary infection. Subsequently, we found her blood was teeming with E coli – the nasty, potentially lethal bacterium. In simple terms, this was a severe case of blood poisoning in someone who was known to have poor kidneys.

Leon was her only next of kin. She had been asking for him until she had collapsed that night.

We had managed to control her chaotic, overly fast heart rate, which otherwise could have killed her within minutes. I had been battling with death all night in trying to bring the high levels of potassium in her blood under control. Unchecked, very high levels can cause cardiac arrest and death. Also, I had had to set up peritoneal dialysis to wash away the impurities in her blood. In spite of all this, she had continued not to look good. Eventually, after a number of attempts, I had been able to contact her son.

Thirty-four hours later, the old lady was nibbling at a biscuit. She had finally responded to treatment. Her blood urea levels were beginning to come down. She had started to produce some urine. Her potassium levels were also decreasing. The infection was coming under control. But she was still far from well. She could deteriorate at any time and die.

She was holding Leon's hand and talking sweetly to him on the ward, delighted that he had come to see her so quickly. I had been summoned by the Ward Sister when this visitor had demanded loudly to see me instantly.

'Why did you give me the wrong impression? Do you know what it cost me to come in a hurry like this? Look at her. How could you possibly have thought that she was dying?'

He was very angry. He looked dishevelled, tired, bald and fat. I noticed he was wearing rainbow striped braces.

'We tried to do the best we could. Thank God, she eventually responded to treatment.'

'I had to cancel the symphony I was scheduled to conduct, drive all night to Montreal, travel first class as there were no seats on economy – and all this because you made a stupid assessment. Hah!' The tirade continued. He did not ask for any information about her condition. It looked to me as though he just wanted to cremate his mother and return to Canada.

'Blame your mother for being alive,' was what I had to stop myself from saying. I did not expect gratitude but there was not even any recognition of our services. Instead, undeserved insults were being heaped on me by the bucketful. Why did I have to bear them quietly?

'I have taken leave for a whole week. I thought that the funeral and all that would have to be arranged. What a waste! What do you want me to do now, hunh?' The tirade finally stopped.

Surprising myself, I replied 'The Old Man of Coniston has inspired many poets and musicians.' After a pause I continued, 'Please excuse me; patients are waiting for me downstairs.' I got up to go. He glared at me. I am sure he would have liked nothing more than to strangle me.

I walked slowly out of the ward. I had not seen my bed for two nights. I had had no lunch that day, apart from munching half a sandwich on the go. I was tired. Surely, I could earn a decent living doing something else. Maybe I should stop being a doctor. Why do people have to be so nasty? I was lost in this reverie when I got into the lift to go down to the outpatient clinics where other patients were waiting for me.

The lift stopped.

'Here you are, Doc,' said someone with a hand thrust out towards me. Startled, I looked up to see Mr Cunningham. Mr Cunningham was in his late forties and had driven a forklift truck at the local shipyard, until he had been made redundant a few years earlier. His wife had been admitted with a massive stroke at the tender age of forty years, probably as a result of taking contraceptive pills. She had remained in a moribund state for the past three weeks. I had been checking how she was doing several times a day. The couple were poor.

Mr Cunningham had seen me many times when he had been visiting his wife. 'Have a drink on me tonight,' he said thrusting a fifty pence coin (the cost of a pint of beer in those days) into my hand. Before I could protest, he was gone.

The roller-coaster of my life as a doctor, flashing past its troughs of despair and peaks of joy, has finally come to a stop after thirty-five years. It was fuelled by the determination to help, heal and comfort. My patients, both dead and alive, are testaments to my honest efforts. I could never have lived any other way.

Sharing this experience with readers has been both cathartic and inspirational, and has turned this retirement into just another break in the journey of my life. I look forward to the future. Perhaps these memories will show me how to reach the next stop.

Also from Hammersmith Press

Suburban Shaman

tales from medicine's frontline

By Cecil Helman
194 pp
ISBN 978-1-905140-08-4

'Cecil Helman is many things: old-fashioned general practitioner, psychiatrist, cultural anthropologist, storyteller, poet and artist – and all this comes together in *Suburban Shaman*, a beautifully written, devastatingly honest (and often very funny) account of an audacious and adventurous life.'

Oliver Sacks, author of *The Man Who Mistook His Wife For A Hat* and *Awakenings*

'A marvellous memoir on the human side of GP practice… His resolutely non-specialist memoir may, I think, turn out to be one of the classics which every medical student *must* read… I don't think anyone since AJ Cronin has expressed so strongly what it is to be embedded in the community as a GP.'

Libby Purves, BBC Radio 4 *Midweek*

'I simply could not put down this extraordinary mixture of stories from the GP's surgery in suburban London… Two clear messages emerge from this book, which should be required reading for every medical student… First, medicine must relearn its heart and soul… Second, there is no certainty in medicine, and no clear answer as to what it is that cures, or fails to cure people… Clearly told, and an extraordinary read, this is a passionate cry for humane medicine.'

Dame Julia Neuberger, *The Independent*

Also available from Hammersmith Press

Playing God

poems about medicine

By Glenn Colquhoun
96 pp
ISBN 978-1-905140-16-9

This remarkable collection of poems by doctor and acclaimed poet, Glenn Colquhoun, is based on his experiences in medical practice, where doctors are often described – or accused of – 'playing God', but where outward confidence hides a constant battle with uncertainty.

Often funny, sometimes serious, always compassionate, the poems explore a range of medical experience that doctors, and anyone who has been in their care, will immediately recognize. Glenn has the ability to find the language that expresses the things we did not even know we were feeling – our helplessness in the face of illness, and our need for hope.